STANDING ON THE OUTSIDE

Tallitha had been determined to forget her past when she came to Brisbane. But it seemed that working for Miles Gilmour would only serve to open the old wounds all over again, and make her vulnerable once more . . .

STANDING ON
THE OUTSIDE

BY

LINDSAY ARMSTRONG

MILLS & BOON LIMITED
15–16 BROOK'S MEWS
LONDON W1A 1DR

First published in Great Britain 1986
by Mills & Boon Limited

© Lindsay Armstrong 1986

Australian copyright 1986
Philippine copyright 1986
This edition 1986

ISBN 0 263 75508 8

Set in Monophoto Plantin 10 on 11½ pt.
01–1186 – 52122

Typeset in Great Britain by
Richard Clay (The Chaucer Press) Ltd,
Bungay, Suffolk

Printed and bound in Great Britain
by Collins, Glasgow

CHAPTER ONE

TALLITHA JONES hesitated over the keyboard of the word processor she was operating and then her hands sank into her lap and she stared longingly towards the smallish window two desks away. But all she could see was a patch of blue sky between two tall, grey buildings, and she sighed. It was her twenty-first birthday—something she had not advertised to anyone, but was now regretting. If you had to spend this important birthday cooped up behind a word processor, she reflected gloomily, wouldn't it be better to have people making a small fuss of you? But then again, what was so important about it? These days, turning twenty-one was not the symbolic event it used to be. Eighteen was more the key-to-the-door age, or even younger . . .

She shivered inwardly, recalling her eighteenth birthday and the daze of misery she'd passed it in. It was one of the reasons she preferred to try to ignore her birthdays, and had succeeded. Until turning twenty-one jumped up and hit me on the head, she thought wryly. Oh well, it will soon be over.

She started to type again.

The typing pool—still called that at Rathdowney, MacPherson & Gilmour—shared the second floor of Rathdowney House with Accounts and Personnel. Tallitha had worked for the pastoral company for nearly a year, but the name had been familiar to her for a lot longer than that. In fact, in the rural communities of far western Queensland where she'd

5

been born and raised, it was a household name. But these days the company bore little resemblance to its origins in the last century when a certain Mr Rathdowney had gone into partnership with a Mr MacPherson, to dabble in livestock sales, land, grain, hides and property. Nowadays it had diversified considerably—into shipping, urban real estate as well as rural, travel, to name a few—and had its own building in downtown Brisbane. Although not on the same scale as the giants of the business, like Elders and Dalgetys, etc., it was a reputable, solid company, if a little old-fashioned.

There were no longer any MacPhersons directly represented on the board but there was, in the position of chairman, a direct descendant of one of the pioneers in the person of Mr Hugo Rathdowney, a rotund, friendly looking man in his fifties, with a deadly eye for a pretty girl—so Tallitha had been warned, although she'd seen no proof of it.

Some time after the original partnership had been formed, a third partner had been added and the position of vice-chairman was currently held by Miles Gilmour, another direct descendant. But Tallitha and a lot of other employees were senior to the vice-chairman—in terms of long service, that was. Because Miles Gilmour had succeeded his father only six months ago, and had gone straight on to the board to take up the position his father had held from the demise of the last Mr MacPherson until his own death.

It had been a matter of quite some gossip that young Mr Gilmour should have been able to do this without ever having worked for the company before. After all, the Gilmours had been traditionally the junior partners and, anyway, the position of vice-chairman was traditionally MacPherson territory—not that there were any MacPhersons available, but still ... It had very soon become apparent, however, that Miles Gilmour was a force to be reckoned with, and that he had plans for Rathdowney, MacPherson & Gilmour which had made all the old hands sit up and gasp, and the slightly old-fashioned pace with which business was conducted in the rather old-fashioned building suddenly come alive and seem urgent.

It had become apparent, too, that some factions of the staff would dearly like Miles Gilmour to fall flat on his face; no one could deny, even those who sided with him, that he had a reputation for being exceedingly impatient and quite devastatingly sarcastic. But then he also was acquiring the reputation for getting things done, and some self-styled experts were claiming that his vision in matters of finance and expansion wasn't so far-fetched after all, but in fact quite brilliant.

All in all, it could be fair to say that Miles Gilmour had shaken the firm inside out in barely six months and that, in the general picking up and dusting off, it was inevitable that he had made himself some enemies, even without the cutting force of his often abrasive personality.

It was not uncommon to hear distinctly bitter remarks made about him and—this always amused Tallitha for some reason—dark comments that the Rathdowneys wouldn't put up with his high and mighty ways for long. But she had discovered that in what was basically a family firm, the doings of the families were vitally interesting to their employees.

She had also discovered that there was one section of the extended family, perhaps a good way to describe the employees, which was always prepared to forgive Miles Gilmour for his excesses. The female section ...

Now if anyone, Tallitha mused on her twenty-first birthday when her thoughts seemed determined to wander, would be positively welcomed for having a deadly eye for a pretty girl, it would be Miles Gilmour. In his mid-thirties, reputedly, the vice-chairman was tall and carried himself with a tigerish, easy grace; he had thick, very dark hair and unusually dark blue eyes. Yes, he was undeniably very good-looking, even in a rage. But to the secret and not so secret anguish of many a girlish, and not so girlish, heart, he remained strictly businesslike in that direction. And many a dream of taming the monster, though not shared by Tallitha, was fading.

Tallitha herself was a girl of below average height with a willowy figure that attracted a lot of male attention although she took care to dress inconspicuously. But it wasn't all that easy when you were blessed with curly red hair, green eyes and a small oval face that could in turn look endearingly tomboyish or, in repose, touchingly Madonna-like. Not that she would have described herself that way; friendly and still with a tendency to look over-eager was how she thought of herself. Definitely not classically beautiful as she admired it in other women. Tall and regal and calm and assured, in other words . . .

'Miss Jones?'

Tallitha looked up. 'Yes, Miss Fortescue,' she said immediately.

Miss Fortescue was office manager but had a commanding presence anyway, although not within Tallitha's concept of classic beauty. But she was tall and, although her figure was bulky, she was always fearsomely groomed with never a grey hair out of place, never a speck or smudge on her glasses, never a crease to mar the immaculate tailoring of her invariably dark-coloured linen dresses or suits. The only things that saved her from a too-masculine appearance were her beautiful hands, with their perfectly manicured oval nails, and the pink rosebud she always wore pinned to her lapel in a little crystal vase-brooch—a tribute, so office gossip had it, to the one love of her life who had died three days before their wedding was to have been.

Tallitha found this bit of gossip fascinating for some reason and often, when she came in contact with Miss Fortescue, tried to imagine her as a young girl in love—not terribly successfully.

However, today, as she found herself the object of Miss Fortescue's rather probing scrutiny, it occurred to Tallitha that the tables might have been turned, that Miss Fortescue was trying to imagine *her* in some other role—with as little success, perhaps.

'Would you come into my office, Miss Jones?' Miss Fortescue said then.

'Of course,' Tallitha murmured, although her heart had started to beat uncomfortably and her mind was rapidly reviewing what she'd done over the past few days that could be harbouring a secret and gross error. But surely I've left those days behind, she thought, remembering those early days when she'd first joined the company as a newly graduated typist from a commercial college taking her first step into the world of business at a slightly more advanced age than normal, but still capable of making mistakes and feeling horribly stupid.

She thought this fleetingly as she stepped into Miss Fortescue's office, for it was not a common occurrence to be invited into this sanctum with its half-glass walls through which that lady could view her domain— Accounts, Personnel and the typing pool.

But perhaps it's about my application for a transfer to Travel, Tallitha thought, sitting down opposite Miss Fortescue. Or perhaps she's going to wish me happy birthday?

She sat up straight, her green eyes suddenly wide and expectant.

'Miss Jones,' Miss Fortescue began, and then hesitated as if having second thoughts.

Tallitha's heart sank and she could contain herself no longer. 'Have I done something wrong?' she queried huskily.

'No.' Miss Fortescue looked briefly surprised. 'No, I'm very pleased with your work. Which is why I'm . . .' She hesitated again.

Tallitha frowned at this second, fatal she thought, hesitation. 'Then I must be . . . redundant? Is that it?' she asked painfully, her small oval face paling suddenly beneath recalcitrant curls which were escaping from the knot on top of her head.

'Of course not, you silly girl!' Miss Fortescue said exasperatedly. 'Does it look as if there are any redundancies? Aren't we all flat out?'

'Well, yes, but I thought it was something you were finding hard to tell me,' Tallitha replied.

Miss Fortescue sighed. 'I am. No, I'm not really. I'm finding it hard to come to a decision, actually, but I don't think I have any choice. You *are* more mature than the others and, well, better for me to have to cope with a replacement from the employment agency who we don't know at all, than him,' she said obscurely and with an odd little grimace.

Tallitha stared at her.

'I'm talking about Mr Gilmour,' Miss Fortescue said, and added briskly, as if she'd relegated her indecision deliberately, 'His private secretary has had a nervous breakdown, it would appear. Consequently I am charged with the task of replacing her, which will not be easy . . . However, be that as it may, I need someone to hold the fort for him in the meantime and that someone will have to be you, Miss Jones,' she said.

Tallitha's mouth fell open. 'Me?' she whispered. 'Do you think that's a good idea?'

For some reason Miss Fortescue found this amusing. 'He doesn't eat people,' she said finally.

Tallitha swallowed. 'He gives a pretty good imitation of it sometimes. What gave his secretary her nervous breakdown?'

A fleeting remnant of a grin curved Miss Fortescue's lips, but she said smoothly, 'It was something personal, I gather.'

'But . . . Well, I've had no experience at . . . at being a private secretary,' Tallitha objected.

'You do have the basic skills though, don't you?' Miss Fortescue glanced at Tallitha's file. 'I mean, you have taken a general secretarial and receptionist course, haven't you?'

'I . . . Yes, but . . .'

'And you did rather well at shorthand, I see.'

'Well, yes, but I haven't had a chance to use it,' Tallitha said somewhat desperately.

'It will come back to you, I'm sure. I'll warn Mr Gilmour that you might be a little rusty for a while.'

Tallitha closed her eyes briefly. 'Miss Fortescue,' she said, 'I really don't think Mr Gilmour . . .'

'Miss Jones,' Miss Fortescue interrupted smoothly, 'I must tell you I've formed the impression that Mr Gilmour is a lot like his father, for whom I used to work once. Hard to please at times because he's a perfectionist, moody, perhaps, but for all that a just and fair man. He will not expect miracles from you.'

Tallitha could think of nothing to say, having seen some evidence of Miles Gilmour's moodiness at a distance. Which had prompted her to think that, if the old saying about distance lending enchantment to the view was true, she'd hate to be any closer. But it also occurred to her that Miss Fortescue was obviously in a bit of a jam, and that, if she turned her down, her expectations of advancement at Rathdowney, MacPherson & Gilmour could suffer.

'I suppose,' she said helplessly, 'I can only try to do my best.'

'I'm sure you will, Miss Jones.'

'When do I start?'

'Now.'

'N-now?' Tallitha stammered, looking down with some despair at her flowered cotton skirt and neat yellow blouse—an unexceptional outfit but nowhere near the elegance private secretary status seemed to require. Although, she had to acknowledge, it was doubtful whether a change of clothes would invest her with that superiority all the private secretaries seemed to have. But they might have given her some assurance and, with a day's notice, at least she could have gone home and spent the night trying to brush up her shorthand.

'Yes, now,' Miss Fortescue said. 'He's expecting you.' She paused and looked at Tallitha acutely. 'One other thing, Miss Jones. Don't get a crush on Mr Gilmour, will you? I've noticed he has that effect on females of the species but I also happen to know he's spoken for, in a manner of speaking.'

Tallitha rose up and said firmly, 'You needn't worry about that, Miss Fortescue. *That* won't be a problem.'

It's like a different world up here, Tallitha thought,

two floors up from Accounts, Personnel and the typing pool, as she hesitated outside the door to Miles Gilmour's suite of offices. Quieter, airier, and much more luxurious.

The door was ajar and she wondered whether she should knock, but she was loaded down with all her possessions from her desk downstairs, mostly crammed into a sharp-cornered metal waste-paper bin upon which she'd snagged many a pair of tights, and some carrier bags of fruit and odds and ends which she'd chosen, on this of all days, to purchase on her way to work. And to knock would mean putting it all down and gathering it all up again, which was why she'd walked up the two flights instead of taking the lift.

Anyway, there won't be anyone in the outer office, will there? she thought.

So she went to lean one shoulder on the door, but unfortunately someone on the other side chose that moment to open it with a flourish and, with a surprised little cry, Tallitha lost her balançe and fell into the room. At least, she started to fall, but encountered the person who had opened the door with the sharp corner of the metal waste-paper bin.

The next few minutes were horribly confused. The recipient of the sharp corner of the bin was obviously as surprised as she was, not to mention possibly physically wounded, from the savage curse he uttered, leaving her in no doubt that it was a he. Not that she was really in doubt anyway, regarding *who*, either. Then they both tried to save themselves but crumpled to the carpet together, although Tallitha dropped the bin, saving them from further injury.

But it didn't alter the fact that she ended up lying half pinned beneath the considerable weight of Miles Gilmour—a furiously surprised and angry Miles

Gilmour. She knew that because, while she was knocked breathless, he was still swearing.

Then she gasped for breath, and suddenly the corners of her mind darkened and she was fighting to free herself, mindlessly twisting and pushing and raking her fingernails along any purchase she could find, fighting like a young tigress.

She must have taken him by surprise because he went quite still for a moment, long enough for her to twist like an eel and free her other hand, which she immediately formed into a fist. But she got no chance to use it for he came to life then and, clamping his hands around her shoulders, got to his knees and ruthlessly dragged her to hers.

'Stop it!' he commanded through his teeth, his dark blue eyes blazing, and he shook her.

But it seemed she couldn't, even as her head flew back painfully. Instead it was if her whole life force was concentrated on escaping as those dark memories flooded her mind. 'Let me *go*,' she wept hysterically, still struggling desperately. 'Let me go!'

He did so, abruptly, and she slumped on to her heels and buried her face in her hands, her breath coming in great gasps and her hair a riot of escaping curls.

They stayed like that for nearly a minute. Then Miles Gilmour got to his feet and leant down to help her to hers.

She stiffened convulsively as she felt his hand on her shoulder.

He said, with a curious mixture of compassion and irony, 'Miss Jones—I presume that's who you are—I can assure you I have not the slightest desire to hurt you in any way. What happened was entirely accidental.'

Tallitha lowered her hands from her face slowly but closed her eyes dazedly.

'Nor can you stay there all day surrounded by a sea of your possessions,' the voice above her continued.

Her lashes flew up and she turned her head from side to side to see, on the carpet, her box of tissues, her oranges, all her odds and ends scattered around. And she remembered being vaguely surprised at the amount of paraphernalia she'd accumulated in her desk downstairs, remembered packing it into the waste-paper bin, the only form of conveyance she'd been able to think of.

Then everything fell into place, including who was standing above her, reasoning with her as if she was a recalcitrant child, and she buried her face in her hands again and tasted tears of despair on her lips. Despair mingled with the feeling of shock that still had her in its grip, and was still sending occasional shudders down the slender curve of her back.

'Come now, Miss Jones,' Miles Gilmour said.

'I'm sorry,' she wept.

'So am I, but this isn't getting us anywhere. Look, I only want to help you up.'

'Th-thank you. Yes, of course,' she stammered, accepting his help this time but with her eyes still streaming and downcast.

Not so surprisingly, she wasn't too steady on her feet and she found herself hanging on to him rather helplessly until he picked her up in his arms, saying steadily, 'I'm just taking you into my office where you can sit down not quite so publicly.'

She tensed, but he ignored it and strode through an inner doorway to deposit her in a chair opposite a broad desk. 'Don't go away,' he said, and she lifted her eyes to see him disappearing through another doorway.

When he reappeared she was sitting huddled unhappily, staring down at her clenched hands.

'I've brought you a glass of water, Miss Jones,' he murmured, and placed a cut-glass tumbler on the desk in front of her. 'But you can have something stronger if you'd like.'

A tinge of colour crept into her pale cheeks and she said huskily, 'Oh, no. Thank you,' and looked up at him directly at last—to gasp at what she saw. He'd been holding a damp-looking handkerchief folded into a pad to his cheek but he took it away as he sat down on the corner of the desk, glanced at it briefly, and then straight into her wide, horrified green eyes. There were three distinct scratches down the side of his face.

'Did I do that?' she whispered. 'Oh, my God!' She scrambled up, her face paling again and her heart starting to beat erratically and her hands to shake.

But a look of determination entered Miles Gilmour's dark blue eyes and he stood up swiftly and gathered her into his arms as she looked around as if for a means of escape. 'Will you relax, Miss Jones,' he ordered. 'No, I'm not letting you go until you do. I know I have a reputation for being somewhat short-tempered, but this is ridiculous! Just calm down.'

Tallitha took an agonised breath and stared up at him with her lips parted. 'I . . . I don't know what to say,' she whispered.

'Then don't,' he murmured, a fleeting grin of amusement curving his lips.

'I . . .'

'Shut up, Miss Jones,' he commanded, but softly.

'I . . .' She bit her lips and her gaze fell slowly until

it was about level with the middle of his tie. Then her chin jerked up again and her lips parted once more but he merely tightened his arms around her slightly until, with a quivering little sigh, she relaxed against him.

He held her like that until her heart was no longer beating like a train and her breathing had steadied. Then he released her but took her hands into his and said, with a funny little smile twisting his lips, 'For a rather little girl, you pack a mighty punch, Miss Jones. You know, I think it might help us both if you were to explain why you got such a fright out there—on one condition.' He looked at her wryly. 'That you promise me not to get so upset again. Otherwise I'll have to call Miss Fortescue and ask her to come up.'

Tallitha licked her lips and it occurred to her, in the midst of her confusion, that Miles Gilmour was being unbelievably nice to her. Which made her feel all the worse. 'I really don't know what got into me,' she said miserably and not quite truthfully. And added hastily, 'But I didn't *think* it was a good idea for me to be your relieving secretary. I was right.' She looked away.

'Oh? Why was that?'

She lifted her shoulders helplessly. 'It was just a feeling I had.'

'Sit down,' he said after a while, and, when she did so obediently, he leant back against the desk and studied her consideringly until she started to colour uncomfortably.

'Are you really saying that *I* frightened the life out of you?' he queried at last with lifted eyebrows. 'But I don't believe we've ever met.'

'Yes, once,' she said lamely. 'When you first arrived.'

'Oh, that.' He smiled slightly. 'I met so many people then I'm afraid I didn't take them all in.

Although,' he looked at her red hair, small face and green eyes with suddenly narrowed eyes, and a wicked little glint entered his dark blue gaze, 'I'm surprised I didn't remember you, Miss Jones.'

Tallitha flinched and closed her eyes briefly. When she opened them, it was to find that all trace of amusement and devilry had left Miles Gilmour's expression. 'That upsets you, too,' he said slowly and thoughtfully. 'I wonder why?'

'I . . . Not really. Well,' she grimaced, 'being a redhead has its disadvantages.'

He looked surprised.

'Well you get called carrots, things like that . . .' She trailed off awkwardly.

'Remind me not to commit that error,' he murmured ruefully. 'But to get back . . .'

'I . . . I did get a fright,' Tallitha interrupted and twisted her hands together.

'Did I hurt you?'

'No! I mean . . . No, but . . .' She looked at him helplessly.

'*Such* a fright?' he queried then with a frown. 'To make you come up fighting for your life?'

'Did I——? I did,' she whispered as he fingered his face. 'I'm so very sorry.'

'Actually I'm happy to hear you say so,' he said with a perfectly straight face, but with that wicked glint in his eyes again. 'You do realise that everyone is going to be wondering what I've done to some poor, helpless female to make her want to scratch my eyes out, don't you, Miss Jones?'

Tallitha stared at him. 'I think it's best if I just go,' she said miserably.

'I didn't say that.' He straightened up. 'Sorry,' he added wryly, 'obviously not the right time to be facetious. So, Miss Jones, I can conclude that my reputation is far worse than I imagined. I must be looked upon as some sort of a monster, obviously.'

Tallitha stared into those amused, dark blue eyes. 'You do . . . You . . . No,' she finished barely audibly as she coloured again and cursed herself inwardly.

'Tell me,' he prompted, 'I'm interested to know what they think of me downstairs. That I'm— autocratic perhaps? Overbearing? Temperamental? Shockingly bad-tempered anyway?' He raised his eyebrows.

'Oh,' she breathed unhappily, 'you're laughing at me.'

'Perhaps,' he admitted with a fleeting grin. 'But let's be honest.' He waited and for the life of her, she couldn't tear her eyes away from that amused, probing, dark blue gaze.

'Well, yes,' she mumbled finally. 'I mean, well, sometimes you are . . . you are . . .'

'All of those things?'

She stared at him helplessly.

He said softly then, 'And that's why you got such a fright? And being a redhead, that's why you came up spitting and fighting?'

She nodded after a moment, just a slight but somehow thankful movement of her head.

There was silence. Then Miles Gilmour said abruptly, 'I don't believe that. I think something rather unpleasant happened to you once and that our little . . . run-in, reminded you of it.'

Tallitha froze. But there was a knock on the door then and a pretty young girl in a waitress's overall and apron wheeled in a trolley, saying brightly, ' 'Morning, Mr Gilmour. Coffee break. I must say . . . Oh! What *have* you done to your face?' she asked with her smile fading and blue eyes wide with concern.

'Morning, Sonia,' Miles Gilmour replied. 'That's just what we need. Make it two cups. This is Miss Jones, by the way. She's to be my relieving secretary.'

'So I heard!' Sonia said, momentarily diverted as Tallitha gasped. 'You'll like her,' she added ingenuously. 'Everyone does. Morning, Tally. I . . .' She stopped and looked at Tallitha rather searchingly.

'Hello, Sonia.'

Sonia frowned slightly and she looked back at Miles Gilmour. 'Your face . . .'

'Oh.' He walked around his desk and sat down. 'My . . . cat got carried away, I'm afraid. It's nothing,' he said gravely.

'Goodness! You want to get him declawed, Mr Gilmour!' Sonia said earnestly.

'I think I will. Can you?'

'Well, I *think* you can. I'd certainly look into it. Or get yourself a dog instead!' She laughed merrily. 'Well, I better get going. You've no idea how impatient some people get for their morning coffee! See you later, Tally!' She turned her trolley then looked back. 'By the way, there's an awful mess out there.'

'Oh, that was Miss Jones, Sonia. She . . . tripped.'

Sonia laughed again. 'You two are having a bad morning!' she called over her shoulder as she left the room and closed the door.

Even Tallitha had to smile, although feebly, at this parting shot. But it faded almost immediately as she asked anxiously, 'Have you got a cat?'

'No.'

'Then . . .?'

'I'm afraid it was all I could come up with at such short notice,' he said apologetically.

'It will be all over the building by lunchtime. And, not everyone's as . . .'

'Naïve as Sonia?' he supplied.

'No.'

'Never mind,' he said consolingly. 'Just think what a diverting titbit it will make. But I'll stick to the cat story if you will, Miss ... By the way, what's Tally short for?'

She told him and like everyone else he asked her what it meant. And as always, she answered that it was just a name her mother had heard and liked, and if it had a meaning she didn't know it.

'Curiouser and curiouser,' Miles Gilmour commented. 'But much more interesting than plain Miss Jones, definitely.' A sudden look of amusement crossed his face. 'I've just thought of the perfect nickname for you, but I won't tell you what it is. I'll keep it for a call to battle.'

'What do you mean?'

'You'll know it when you hear it,' he said perfectly seriously. 'Then *you* can regard it as a call to arms. Talking of which,' his eyes sobered, 'what was it?'

'W-what was what?'

'My dear ...' All of a sudden a steely note entered his voice. 'I'm not a fool and Miss Fortescue assures me you aren't, either. I think you got an awful fright just now because you were once either mugged or assaulted or raped or ... run over by a bus,' he said drily. 'But whatever, I'd rather you were honest with me. I find that's the best way to be, frankly.'

Tallitha stared at him, her green eyes shadowed. 'Yes,' she whispered at last.

He said nothing for a time, just studied her face narrowly. Then he smiled, but not as if he found her amusing; rather, it was a communicaton of warmth and compassion and it stunned Tallitha queerly.

Then he said, 'It's all right. That's all I wanted to

know. I don't intend to drag the details out of you. Why don't you finish your coffee and, if you feel OK, we might get some work done.'

'But I don't understand!' she said huskily. 'I mean, how you can still want me to be your relieving secretary—after this?' She opened her hands expressively.

'Didn't they tell you? I'm also very unpredictable.'

'I . . .'

'Yes?'

'I . . . I . . . Well I'm very grateful,' she said helplessly, 'but . . .'

He burst out laughing. 'Oh, I wouldn't be too hasty, Tallitha. You might find yourself yet regretting this appointment. I really am all the things they say about me, you know.'

A faint spark of indignation lit Tallitha's eyes. 'I was only trying to . . . Perhaps you could conceal it?' Your face?' she said, changing tack mid-sentence, and unsure why she should suddenly be feeling reproachful and indignant. After all, he could have fired me, she told herself. If only he hadn't found it quite so amusing and hadn't lured me into virtually agreeing that he was all those awful things. And *then* to hit the nail on the head, more or less!

Her lashes flew up as he spoke. 'I'm sure it's too late for that,' he replied, with a meaningful look at the door through which Sonia had passed.

'Too late for here, yes,' Tallitha agreed, 'but for away from the office. You can get these concealer sticks that seem to work.' She bit her lip.

'Thank you, but no,' he said with some irony. 'How do you know they work anyway?' he asked, scanning her fair, perfect skin with interest.

'I haven't used one myself,' she confessed, 'but Li

. . . one of the girls in the typing pool came to work one day with this awful . . .' She stopped.

'Awful what?'

'Mark on her neck?' Tallitha said hastily.

'Love bite, you mean?'

Tallitha coloured for no reason except that she was heartily wishing she'd never brought the subject up, for it was obviously affording Miles Gilmour more amusement. 'Yes,' she said stiffly. 'And one of the other girls leant her a concealer stick. But I suppose it would look odd on a man. I was only trying to think of ways to help,' she added in a dignified little voice.

'Too late, too late, Tally-ho!' he said softly.

Her mouth dropped open and all of a sudden her eyes flashed green fire as the nickname he'd devised for her sank in.

But he said with a detached air of interest, before she got a chance to assemble her wits, 'So you do have a temper to match your red hair, Tallitha?'

Tallitha stared at him angrily but managed to bite her lip on the hot words that bubbled up within. Then, curiously, it struck her that this incredible sequence of events was happening to her on her twenty-first birthday, of all days, and she thought suddenly, how unfair can life be, and blinked desperately to no avail.

'Oh come now, Miss Jones,' Miles Gilmour said a shade wearily as he critically observed one sparkling teardrop splash on to her blouse. 'I must warn you that if there's one thing I loathe it's . . .'

'Women who cry,' Tallitha interrupted unsteadily, and searched through the pockets of her skirt for her handkerchief. 'So do I,' she agreed and blew her nose. 'I don't seem to be able to help it sometimes, though. And I wasn't crying because of *you*.'

Miles Gilmour lifted a sceptical eyebrow. 'No? Personally, I've always suspected it was a time-honoured ploy when the going got a bit rough. But,' he paused and his dark blue gaze flickered over her, 'perhaps we're overstating the case. I mean,' he said when she looked blank, 'that we're confusing women with girls.'

Tallitha laughed in spite of herself. 'No we're not. I'm twenty-one. Now.'

He said after a moment, 'That's still a very young woman and I must say you don't look it, but why so bitter about it?'

'Bitter? Am I? Not really. It's just that it's . . . It doesn't matter!'

He didn't reply, just sat looking at her dispassion-ately, but the message came over loud and clear—in other words, they had an agreement now, didn't they?

Tallitha took a breath and moved restlessly. Then she said exasperatedly, 'It's my birthday today if you must know! My twenty-first, and all I've done is come to work like any other day, only unlike any other day, I've got myself into . . . into this mess!' she said, this time with a great deal of bitterness which was in no way lessened when Miles Gilmour leaned back in his chair and started to laugh heartily.

She stood up, every line of her small figure taut and angry and hurt.

'No,' he said then and got up to come round to her. 'Don't look like that. I'm sorry for everything and I agree these things shouldn't happen to you on your twenty-first birthday. I also think it's enough to make *anyone* cry, but I wasn't to know and, if you'll only let me, I'll seriously try to make amends,' he said gravely.

'How?' Tallitha asked suspiciously, her eyes still bright and angry. 'You're only teasing me again!'

'No, I'm not!' he vowed. 'From now on I pledge myself to be the perfect boss—polite, patient, punctual, understanding—what else? You name it and I'll be it,' he said with not a flicker of hilarity disturbing his expression.

Sparkling green eyes stared up into those very dark, very serious, blue ones and Tallitha Jones heard herself saying confusedly, 'You can be nice, I think. I mean you *are* teasing me, but nicely. Oh! I didn't mean . . .'

'Nonsense,' Miles Gilmour interrupted rather wryly. 'I told you—I really am the ogre you suspected I was. When it's no longer your twenty-first birthday I'm sure you'll find you were right in the first place, so don't say I didn't warn you!' But his eyes were laughing again as he stood back, although he said then, 'Perhaps we should get some work done now, Miss Jones?'

She agreed shyly, but it occurred to her not much later that this new dimension to Miles Gilmour could be as hard to handle as what she'd already known about him. I mean—she tried to qualify the thought to herself—what do I mean? But all she could come up with was that her temporary boss was undoubtedly quite a handful, whether he was being nice or not. And that she didn't seem to be equipped to cope very well . . .

But that confusing day was not over, she discovered, when, at five minutes to five he came into the outer office and told her that Miss Fortescue would like to see her before she left for the day. 'Just a . . . technicality, I gather, Tallitha,' he said. 'Off you go. See you tomorrow!'

The technicality turned out to be a heart-shaped birthday cake with twenty-one candles on it, a bottle of champagne and all the girls from the typing pool and Accounts and Personnel gathered to toast her.

'How . . . how did you know?' Tallitha enquired of Miss Fortescue when the excitement had died down a bit.

'Not from you,' Miss Fortescue said a little drily. 'Why didn't you tell us? It's not every day you turn twenty-one.'

'That's true,' Tallitha agreed ruefully. 'So it must have been Mr Gilmour?'

'That's for me to know and you to wonder about,' Miss Fortescue said regally, and sipped her champagne.

'By the way, talking of Mr Gilmour,' Linda of the love bite butted in, as she had a habit of doing, 'what's happened to his face?'

All eyes swivelled to Tallitha, even Miss Fortescue's.

'He said his cat did it,' she muttered.

'Well I for one don't believe that!' Linda said in ringing tones. 'I believe it was a *woman*. But the really strange thing is, Mary-Lou at the front desk swears he didn't have those scratches when he came to work this morning!'

'Must have had a mysterious encounter with a lady after he came to work,' another girl chimed in, and added, 'I do *envy* you, Tally. He's just gorgeous. What wouldn't I give for the opportunity to scratch his eyes out!'

This brought several shocked protestations and then comfortable and animated discussion on men with a capital M! Only Miss Fortescue and Tallitha didn't contribute to it, although Miss Fortescue listened with a funny little smile on her lips. Then she put her glass down and said, 'That's it, girls. Those of us who are taking Miss Jones to dinner had better be leaving, they won't keep our table for ever. Come along, Miss Jones,' she said and added, 'That's the penalty for trying to keep your birthday a secret!'

'Oh ... thank you,' Tallitha said breathlessly. 'I don't know what I've done to deserve this, but thank you all so much!'

CHAPTER TWO

TALLITHA put herself to bed that night still feeling somewhat bewildered but not unhappily so. For a day that had appeared to be taking a disastrous course, it had ended on a surprisingly high note and she regretted having been so coy about her twenty-first birthday. They were all so *nice*, she mused. I hope they didn't think I was sulking.

She grimaced and reached out to switch off her bedside lamp but didn't. Instead, she hitched her pillow up a bit higher and looked around her room seeking the feeling of pride and warmth it always gave her.

It was small, a bed-sitter in fact, but with a separate kitchen and bathroom, and her own veranda. Far from being the traditional gloomy bed-sitter, it glowed with life and colour. The walls were painted a Chinese yellow and along one of them, gleaming, white-painted shelves ran the full length and were crammed with her colourful possessions—records and a small stereo set she was still paying off; books; odd bits of pottery— she could never resist interesting glazes and shapes; a jade green mug crammed with white daisies from the garden; pot plants; her four differently shaped sun hats with their bright silk sashes—something else she couldn't resist.

Her window was curtained with frilly voile drapes and a pink tasselled blind, and in a corner beside it stood a tall, old vase that had a crack in it which was faced to the wall, and beautiful, fierce, red Chinese dragons around it.

On the floor there was wall-to-wall oatmeal Berber carpeting, which was in fact composed of offcuts, but unless one knew where to look the seams weren't visible. Her bed, which doubled as a sofa during the day, had a fitted floor-length spread with box pleats in a heavy linen with a shadowy pattern of geranium-pink clouds on a soft, sherbet-green background. Her only armchair had a cane and basket-work frame and plump, full cushions covered in the same material as the bedspread, and beside it there was a white-painted desk with bright brass handles on the drawers, and a pink angle-lamp. There was also a restored, white-painted bentwood chair.

Beside the bed-sofa there was a low cabinet with louvred doors which served as a bedside table and into which went her frilled pillow during the day. On it stood an old-fashioned brass alarm clock and an exquisite little alabaster lamp with a pink silk shade which she'd picked up for a song in a dim, dusty antique shop.

Above the bed hung a large, gold-framed print, that looked like a painting, of a white farmhouse surrounded by hazy golden paddocks beneath a dusty blue sky.

Fortunately, because it wasn't a large room, the bathroom, which had originally been a laundry, had a whole wall of cupboards and that was where she kept her clothes and all her other belongings, like the old-fashioned sewing machine upon which she made so many of her clothes, and had made the bedcover and matching cushions, the frilled broderie-anglaise pillowcases she used to match the sheets she'd trimmed, the yellow birdcage cover with its elegant frill.

But all of the comfort and the colour had come after she'd rented the 'flatlet', as the taciturn landlord who

had divided his sprawling old house into flats and
flatlets after his wife had died, called it.

The only thing that had stopped her from rejecting
the place on sight had been the low rent, far lower
than she'd hoped to find. Then she'd walked out on to
the veranda, which was quite private, and noticed that
the garden was well kept and full of flowering
perennials and that there was a poinciana tree laden
with scarlet blossoms in the middle of the lawn—for
that matter the whole suburb of Ashgrove on that
spring day had been alive with purple jacarandas and
scarlet poinciana blooms.

She had hesitated and turned back to the bare,
lifeless room—the flatlet was unfurnished apart from
stove, fridge and washing machine. 'Could I paint it?'
she'd asked tentatively. At her own expense, had been
the taciturn reply.

She had thought some more, taking into account
that there was a bus stop half a block away, shops
handy and a library down the road, and finally she
had driven a bargain with the landlord, who didn't live
on the premises and affected a cynical, world-weary
attitude towards tenants as if they were the lowest of
the low: if he undertook certain repairs in the kitchen
and bathroom, she would paint the place at her own
expense. The deal had been struck and she'd lived
there ever since, gradually making it more comfortable.

And she'd come to share some of the landlord's
world-weariness concerning tenants as she'd witnessed
some strange people coming and going from the other
flats, but, since she had her own private entrance with
a stout lock, they didn't really bother her. She had also
earned his grudging respect because she enjoyed
pottering around her part of the garden, because she

was always prompt with the rent and because she kept her flatlet so well. He insisted on making three-monthly inspections, which she couldn't really blame him for. Whether he appreciated the yellow walls, the turquoise bathroom and the vivid scarlet wallpaper strewn with violets that she'd done the kitchen in, he'd never said.

And it had become more than a home to her, she reflected as she lay with her head comfortably pillowed on the night of her twenty-first birthday, still too keyed up, after a day of days for more reasons than one, to sleep. It had become like a spiritual haven where she could dream dreams that now, incredibly, might even materialise one day. A place where she could surround herself with colour and light and, most of all, the permanence that had been so lacking in her childhood.

Only, she mused, I might have lost it all today, mightn't I?

She stared up at the old, decorated ceiling then turned over and buried her face in the pillow. I'd thought I'd forgotten—I haven't thought of it for ages. Not like that, not as if it was going to happen again. What awful tricks your subconscious mind can play on you. But he was heavy, and I suppose that's what did it. To do what I *did*, though . . .

She shivered and lifted her head to lay her cheek on her hand as she fiddled with the pillowcase frill, her mind conjuring up a devastatingly accurate image of Miles Gilmour's handsome face, but marred now by those scratches. And she thought, he'd have been quite entitled to fire me . . . I really can't help wondering why he was so kind about it. Mind you, he's going to have to live with them for quite a few days which probably won't amuse him for ever. But it was kind of him to organise the birthday party—I'm sure it was him . . .

She sighed then and yawned and reached out once more to put the lamp off but her budgerigar in his elegant cage cheeped, disgruntled, and she pushed the bedclothes away with a grin. 'Did I forget to cover you up, Mason?' she said. 'There you go. Say good night, Mama!'

But although she hovered for a while, reflected against the yellow wall with her legs and feet bare, Mason preserved a stolid silence.

Maybe he's still too young to talk, she thought.

One week later the impossible happened.

Tallitha had not the slightest inkling it was going to because as she'd expected, and Miles Gilmour had predicted, it had not all been plain sailing between them. In fact there had been a few quite uncomfortable encounters, although, curiously, only one over his scarred face—until the real explosion came!

Another curious thing she had discovered was that those scratches seemed to make him even more attractive to her sex. At least, so she'd gathered from the comments she'd heard.

But he had stuck to the cat story, only allowing himself to show any ire towards her when even she had decided that, if one more person asked him about his face, she might scream. The fatal question on this occasion had come from a friend, Tallitha had gathered when Miles had come out of his office to greet him. A cheerful, middle-aged man who had given Tallitha the eye and then, as soon as her boss had appeared, had uttered the words with a sort of delighted incredulity. 'I say, what on earth's happened to your face, old mate?'

Miles Gilmour had directed a stormy dark blue gaze at Tallitha and replied harshly, 'I had the misfortune to tangle with a tigress.'

The other man had laughed delightedly and looked extremely speculatively at Tallitha before he had murmured, 'Do introduce me to her. I could do with a tigress in my tank—my love life's been jolly tame lately.'

Tallitha had winced and coloured but, beyond grinding his teeth visibly, Miles Gilmour had only ushered his jovial mate into his office without a backward glance. He had slammed the door, however, and for the rest of that day had been curt to the point of rudeness, and so impatient she'd gone home feeling as limp as a wet rag. Not to mention rather cynical of Miss Fortescue's promise that Miles Gilmour would not expect miracles from her.

But the next morning had seen him restored to a better humour, although he didn't go so far as to apologise. Not that Tallitha had really expected him to, but she had gone into work determined to show him somehow or other that she resented being treated like that. He took the wind right out of her sails from the word go by directing her a charming smile as soon as they first met.

Involuntarily mollified, and annoyed because she was, she had sat at her desk opening the mail and wondered how he could do it with just a smile.

But if one thing had become considerably clearer to her during that first week, it was that Miles Gilmour was a man of many facets. Not only could he charm with a smile when he chose—if anything that was a black mark against him in Tallitha's estimation—there were other things about him that . . . well, intrigued her, she had to admit.

One of them was his treatment of Sonia, the tea girl. If anyone could be called a dumb blonde, Sonia rightfully could. At only nineteen, she'd already worked for the company for five years and possibly would be content to be a tea lady for the rest of her life. Mainly becasue she'd adopted everyone who worked for Rathdowney, MacPherson & Gilmour and spent a large part of her time acutely concerned about inter-office rivalries, not to mention personal problems—Sonia was extremely kind-hearted. She was also something of an expert on what went on behind the scenes, particularly in connection with members of the board. How she acquired her information was something of a mystery and often scoffed at, but time and time again, to some people's fury, Sonia's gossip was laced with grains of truth.

If anyone could have driven Miles Gilmour up the wall, Tallitha would have nominated Sonia as a prime example. But instead he was gentle and friendly with her, often made her laugh. And while Tallitha hated the few people who poked sly fun at Sonia behind her back, it irked her oddly to think that her boss wasn't one of them.

Another matter for intrigue was his flair for his job. Most matters of high finance ended up on Miles Gilmour's desk and he took decisions concerning millions of dollars with an almost lazy, bored air. Although, if you looked close enough, you would discover a glint in those dark blue eyes that wasn't bored at all. In fact, Tallitha decided, it was the glint of a very clever, shrewd brain at work. Of course there were the other times when there was *nothing* bored or lazy about him at all, the times when someone around him didn't measure up, the times when she trembled inwardly despite herself, and waited for the explosion. And hoped to God it wasn't her turn next.

But, inexorably, her turn came on the last day of the first week. Curiously, she'd spent a relatively peaceful morning looking back on the week and deciding that she'd coped rather well. She'd even indulged—it had been a very quiet morning—in some grateful thoughts about her boss, and found herself speculating on a bit of gossip she'd overheard in the canteen the day before. Was Miles Gilmour going to step shortly into Hugo Rathdowney's shoes? In other words, be appointed chairman? Oh, not for years yet, someone had offered, and anyway there was a Rathdowney son, wasn't there? True, but comparing him to Miles Gilmour, a wit had said, was like comparing a sheep to a tiger.

Being a little sensitive on the subject of tigers, Tallitha had prepared to depart, but the gossip she was overhearing had then turned to a general discussion on the virtues of the Rathdowneys and the Gilmours, and why some people considered there would always be a Rathdowney in the company just as there would always need to be a Gilmour. It seemed they brought quite different talents with them, the two families. The Rathdowneys still had their roots out west and still had a feel for the land that was invaluable to what was, after all, still the backbone of the company.

But is it? someone had argued. The general consensus had been that the rural side of the company *was* very important to it. Whereas, the discussion had finally gone on, the Gilmours were a different cup of tea. They'd been brought in for their business acumen; they'd always been a prominent Brisbane family with no roots out west but a flair for trade and commerce, be it in hides or stocks and shares . . .

Then the discussion had switched back to the Rathdowneys, the Gilmours and the MacPhersons and odd snippets of gossip were trotted out—the MacPhersons and the Gilmours, for example, had a history of personal conflict, and did you know that the present Mrs Rathdowney, matriarch and said to be a driving force behind Hugo, not to mention mother of a fledgeling son—did you know she was a MacPherson? Well, not that closely related but related all the same . . . Wouldn't it be interesting to know what she thought of Miles Gilmour becoming chairman . . .?

'What I'd like to know,' an amused voice had said then, 'is what *happened* to the MacPhersons?'

Tallitha had wondered that, too, and had found herself wondering then with a small grin whether Miles Gilmour realised what a hornet's nest of gossip and speculation he had stirred up. But a glance at her watch had told her that she couldn't wait to hear what had happened to the MacPhersons.

The next day, though, she was still thinking about the conversation as she took her lunch hour, but not in the canteen. But the sight that greeted her eyes when she got back from lunch drove most coherent thoughts from her mind.

She had a small filing cabinet in her office and Miles Gilmour was delving into it like a man possessed, pulling out files at random, it seemed, and casting them to the floor in disgust. As she made a small sound, he swung round and his expression was so murderously angry, she dropped her basket from sheer fright. Unfortunately she'd bought six oranges during her lunchtime and they rolled out of their packet all over the floor.

Miles Gilmour observed this for a moment then raised a taut face and remarked, 'What do you do with them? Make glacé fruit as a sideline? Or are they a secret beauty recipe of yours? Do you . . . extract the juice to preserve your very nice complexion?' But in fact the look with which he summed up her complexion was far from complimentary, it was instead quite withering.

'I . . . I eat them!'

'Oh do you! Then it must be a new diet. If I remember rightly about five days ago you dropped a ton of them all over the floor too.'

'No. Six. I happen to like oranges.'

'That much is obvious, my dear Miss Jones,' he said caustically. 'And I really don't mind your . . . fixation with oranges.' He said it as if it was an unpleasant perversity of Tallitha's. 'I just wish you wouldn't keep dropping them all over the place.'

'I didn't . . . I don't have . . . They are good for . . . Are you looking for something?' Tallitha asked, managing to steady her voice only by a severe effort of will.

'Actually I am. The McIntyre Limited file. What the devil have you done with it?' he replied in a hard, clipped voice.

'Nothing . . . nothing,' Tallitha said, mentally reviewing all the files she'd dealt with recently. 'Nothing . . . er . . . Have you looked under M . . .' A silly thing to say of course.

'Why wouldn't I look under bloody M?' Miles Gilmour asked coldly. 'Did you think I'd look for it under I? Or is that the new system? Dispense with the Macs and file them under . . .'

'Not at all,' Tallitha said stiffly. 'That would be stupid, wouldn't it?'

'You tell me,' he said sardonically, and eyed her person, clad today in a neat cream linen skirt and toffee-coloured silk blouse, from head to toe as if she was the personification of stupidity.

She gritted her teeth, willing herself not to wilt literally under his scathing, dark blue gaze. 'Will you let me look for it then?'

He stood aside. 'Be my guest.'

There was no McIntyre in the Macs or the Ms and the fact that he still stood there, leaning against the wall with his arms folded and his eyes smouldering—a picture of arrogant impatience—didn't help.

'It's not here,' she said helplessly, after double checking and finding it very difficult not to feel flustered and hot.

'You surprise me,' Miles Gilmour said.

'You haven't ... You wouldn't have it in your office?'

'No.'

Tallitha looked round, but she'd cleared her desk before going to lunch. 'I'll have to go right through the files, then, but that'll take a few minutes ...' She stopped and bit her lip.

'So?' he queried, as if dealing with an imbecile child.

'W-well, you don't have to wait.'

'How kind you are, Miss Jones,' he said mockingly. 'All the same I will.'

Tallitha stared at him. 'Is it that urgent?'

Those dark blue eyes narrowed and he opened his mouth to demolish her totally, Tallitha just knew, and she was spurred to greater effort. 'What I mean is ... you make me nervous standing there like that,' she said rather shakily.

'Oh, I do apologise, Miss Jones,' Miles Gilmour

replied ironically. 'We can't have that, can we? Indeed no. Nervousness can lead to fright, can't it? And we know what might happen then, don't we? Did you ever think of taking out a black belt? Karate? That kind of stuff. It would be fairer, you know, than trying to claw someone's eyes out. But don't let me even tempt you! I shall remove myself.' And he stalked into his office and closed the door, not quietly.

Reproach, indignation and, oddly, a sudden spark of black humour lit Tallitha's green eyes as the door slammed and she turned back to the filing cabinet. I'm not sorry I did that to you, she mused. I'm really not sorry . . .

But due to a veritable barrage of interruptions, it was nearly an hour before she could say with certainty that the McIntyre file was not in the cabinet, misfiled or otherwise. Like the MacPhersons—how strange, she thought—it appeared to have disappeared off the face of the earth.

Miles Gilmour received this information with tight lips and a dangerous glint in his eye. 'Then you'd better find where it is, Miss Jones,' he said softly. 'I need that file.'

'But I don't know where to look,' Tallitha replied honestly. 'Unless . . .' She looked around his office.

'It's *not* here. I have looked and it's not here,' he said, articulating very precisely.

'Well, the thing is, I *don't* remember the name,' she protested, getting that hot, flustered feeling again. 'If I'd done anything with it, I'm sure I would. When did you last see it?'

'It was on my desk two days ago. It was in the filing basket.'

'Then I would have filed it. What else would I . . .' She stopped as he stood up and started to walk around the desk. 'I'll . . .' She swallowed. 'I'll go and have another look,' she whispered, and fled.

Once in the safety of the outer office, with the door closed, she leant back against it and breathed deeply several times. Now don't let him get to you, she told herself. I *know* I had nothing to do with that file!

Then her door opened with the briefest knock and Mr Rathdowney himself walked in. 'Ah, Miss . . . er . . .?' He looked at her enquiringly and frowned. 'Do I know you?'

'Not actually,' Tallitha answered. 'I'm Miss Jones, Mr Gilmour's relieving secretary. Sir.'

Mr Rathdowney smote his bespectacled forehead with a pudgy hand. 'That's right! Poor girl had a nervous breakdown, didn't she? His other one, I mean. Must say Miles knows how to pick lookers—my first sweetheart,' he said with a roguish smile, 'had hair just your colour. And a temper to match,' he added. Then he screwed his eyes up in a peculiarly abstracted manner and patted his cheek several times and said, 'Dear me, he *said* his cat scratched him, Miles did, but I found that hard to believe at the time. Well! So you have a temper to go with your hair, too, Miss . . . er . . . Jones. Good for you, although I'm surprised—what I mean is, perhaps you should do it in a less visible spot next time. Yes, definitely, I would advise that.'

Tallitha stared at him, consumed by a horrible mixture of embarrassment and the feeling that she'd strayed into a madhouse. She opened her mouth weakly to deny the charge but it appeared she wasn't expected to comment, for Mr Rathdowney flourished a manila folder at her and went on in the next breath, 'I came, by the way, to restore this file to Miles. Borrowed it the other day. Happened to be on his desk. No one about at the time.'

Tallitha saw the name of McIntyre on the file and acted, she thought afterwards, with the promptness of the righteous or in the manner of someone shouting, 'I *told* you so,' without actually saying it . . .

She swung round and opened the inner door with a flourish, saying, 'Mr Gilmour's here himself, sir. Mr Rathdowney to see you, Mr Gilmour,' she added sweetly, as Miles Gilmour turned an irate face towards the door.

'Oh well, might as well return it in person,' Mr Rathdowney said genially, as Tallitha ushered him in and closed the door with an entirely demure, downcast expression.

It wasn't until five o'clock that Miles Gilmour made any further mention of the McIntyre file. Then he strolled into the outer office where Tallitha was packing up for the night, and sat down on the corner of her desk.

He had the jacket of his elegant grey suit slung over one arm and he leisurely adjusted the sleeves of his blue and white pin-striped shirt, which had been pushed untidily up his forearms, buttoned them and his collar and straightened his navy blue silk tie, ran a hand through his thick, dark hair and gently swung one foot encased in the finest black calf. He did all this while subjecting Tallitha to a contemplative yet thoroughly comprehensive look which she found utterly nerve-racking.

Then he said idly, 'I suppose you're expecting me to apologise?'

It struck her later, though, that for some reason her nerves always reacted strangely towards this man. For she undoubtedly looked at him innocently and enquiringly as if she had not the slightest idea what he was talking about.

A glint of amusement lit his dark blue eyes. And he said softly, 'Oh, come on, Tally-ho! I'd really rather you didn't stay cross with me.'

'I'm not cross with you,' she said stiffly. 'For one thing, it's not my place to be.'

'It didn't stop you once before,' he said with a grin, and fingered his face where the scratch marks had all but healed.

'That was quite different . . .' She stopped abruptly.

'You mean, I was in the wrong then but not now?' he queried.

She started to speak, then determinedly closed her lips and directed him a furious, speaking, green glance instead.

He laughed. 'If looks could kill I'm lucky to be alive. Dear Tallitha, I do most sincerely apologise for being—what was it? Oh yes, impossibly overbearing. And of course you were quite *right* to put me in my place so effectively, I deserved it and will try to mend my ways. How about it?'

All this was said with perfect gravity but to Tallitha it was so obviously tongue-in-cheek, she promptly forgot her resolve to have no further truck with the conversation and remarked acidly, 'You are impossible, you know. Don't think I'm deceived for one minute!'

'Well, I didn't think you were really,' he replied mildly. 'But actually I *am* sorry I was so unpleasant. It's a habit with me, unfortunately.'

Tallitha considered for a moment, then said with a trace of indignation, 'Now you're making me feel as if I was in the wrong.'

'We seem to be utterly at cross purposes,' he murmured with lurking laughter in his eyes. 'But at least you're talking to me again.'

'I . . . I never stopped talking to you,' she protested.

'You tried to just now,' he reminded her. 'And ever since Mr Rathdowney returned the file, which is nearly all afternoon, you've treated me with such icy civility, it was as bad as not being talked to.'

Tallitha opened her mouth to deny this but found herself grinning shamefacedly. 'Oh, all right,' she said weakly. 'I *was* cross with you.'

'But now I'm forgiven?'

'Oh . . . yes! Do you know, you really surprise me sometimes.' She looked at him candidly.

'You've indicated that before,' he said wryly.

Tallitha coloured faintly.

'As a matter of fact,' Miles Gilmour went on, 'you surprise me, too.'

'I do?'

'Yes.'

'In what way?' Tallitha asked, curious despite herself.

'In the way you've coped with the monster,' he said with a fleeting grin.

'It's only been a week . . .'

'What do they say? A miss is as good as a mile.'

'I don't understand.'

'Well,' he said gravely, 'put it this way. One week is quite long enough for me to conceive a possibly irrational aversion to a secretary. Actually two hours is generally all I need.'

'I . . . still don't understand,' she said a little breathlessly, searching his face incredulously.

He stood up and shrugged on his jacket. 'Of course it's not Travel, which I understand is your ultimate goal, but there could be some travelling involved. And it's very well paid. Much better paid than you would be in Travel, assuming there was an opening, which there isn't, at present. How about it?' he said for the second time.

'You mean, you want me to be your secretary?' Tallitha whispered. 'Your *permanent* secretary . . .'

'Indeed I do. Why not?'

'I . . . I don't feel like one,' she said. 'I don't feel *qualified*. I don't believe this,' she said then, her green eyes dazed. 'I thought it would take *years* of experience. I thought I would be the *last* person you would—I mean, want.'

'Funnily enough,' he said with a funny little smile, 'my wants are quite simple. You can do all the basics, you obviously resent being walked all over, which is a big plus, believe me . . .'

'Then why . . . Then *why* . . .'

'Do I do it? he supplied as her voice failed her. 'I think I was born with a contrary streak, probably.'

Tallitha stared at him. 'But my shorthand is still rather slow,' was all she could think of to say.

'Practise will make perfect.'

'H-have you spoken to Miss Fortescue about it?' she stammered.

'Yes. She was very relieved, as a matter of fact. Don't you *want* the job, Tallitha?' he queried with a probing glance.

Tallitha closed her eyes and wondered if she should pinch herself. For she well knew that this was an incredible stroke of good fortune. Financially, status-wise, from the point of view of job satisfaction in most respects, it was a leap up the ladder of mammoth proportions. An *entrée* to the small, select band of female staff whom the girls from the typing pool admired from afar, and aspired to be like in matters of dress and every other way. And from the point of view of further job prospects, in time it could open up great vistas. With experience as private secretary to a director of Rathdowney, MacPherson & Gilmour ... Well, for a girl from beyond the Black Stump, it was incredible. In just a year ...

Her eyes flew open and, to her dismay, Miles Gilmour was swimming in a mist of tears.

'Oh damn,' she said helplessly. 'There I go again. Do you want to change your mind?'

He laughed and touched her cheek lightly. 'You had me worried for a moment. No, I don't.' Then he sobered and looked at her a little curiously. 'It's obviously a big thing for you. I hope I live up to it,' he said with a trace of irony.

'Yes it is,' she agreed, and blew her nose.

He sat down on the desk again. 'It shouldn't be, you know,' he said slowly. 'You're bright enough. Want to tell me why it's moved you to tears?'

'I ...' Tallitha put her hanky away and smiled tremulously. 'I guess it's because of my background. All I was ... conditioned to expect was a life of domesticity, but the hard side of it. Scrubbing someone else's floors and washing nappies for someone else's babies—that kind of thing.' She grimaced.

'Out west?'

'Yes. My mother was a professional housekeeper, you might say. Not by choice but because my father died, leaving her broke with me to support, and she was good at that kind of thing, a good cook and so on. But she wasn't very strong so I used to help. We moved around a lot from station to station ...'

'Why was that?' he interrupted.

Tallitha shrugged. 'Out west you have the good years and the bad ones—times when you can afford a housekeeper and times when you can't. That was mainly why. Then she died and I . . . I suppose it suddenly dawned on me that I didn't have to stay . . .' She broke off and looked down at her hands.

'Go on,' he said. 'Or can I guess? You suddenly began to think of *not* spending the rest of your life that way?'

'Yes,' she said. 'I . . . came to the big smoke, which my mother would have hated . . .'

'Why?'

Tallitha hesitated, then she said honestly, 'She was—I loved her very much, but she was rather naïve and old-fashioned, and very religious. She believed cities abounded with sin. But I don't think they have a monopoly on it by any means.'

There was a short silence.

'I mean, people are people wherever they are, aren't they?' she said.

'In general, yes,' he agreed after a pause. 'Do you remember your father?'

'Only hazily. He was a stockman. He got caught in a bushfire . . . But I've still got all his books. He used to love to read and he had cartons of them which we carted around wherever we went. My mother used to grumble about them and threaten to burn them— particularly when I couldn't be found because I'd sneaked away with one. But I think she was rather happy really that I'd inherited his passion for reading.'

'So you came to the city with your father's books and little else?' he hazarded.

'Yes. And my mother's sewing machine. And I took a typing course and took in contract sewing, and generally,' she smiled impishly, 'got rid of the hayseeds. Which is why I'm a bit bowled over right now,' she said huskily. 'I . . . I can't think how to thank you . . .'

But Miles Gilmour raised his eyebrows laughingly. 'Don't,' he said. 'I think our relationship is on a very sound footing and we shouldn't allow any syrupy sentiments to cloud it. You earned the job, you got it. Right?'

'Right,' she said, somewhat tearfully but happily.

'Why don't you go out and celebrate instead?' he suggested. 'Got a boyfriend?'

'No. But I might even persuade Mason to talk to me. When I tell him about this, he's bound to break his silence!'

Later that night, when she'd calmed down and was able to think objectively about her incredible good fortune, she found herself thinking more in fact of Miles Gilmour himself. And how it was a mistake to pre-judge people. Because beneath that forceful, dominating, sometimes savage personality, there was a streak of warmth and kindness that still confused and bewildered her.

Did they know? she pondered. All those girls in the typing pool. How could they? I certainly didn't, but then I'm not exactly famed for my perceptions in that line, am I?

'Am I?' she said slowly out loud to Mason, but when he maintained a stony silence she threatened to exchange him for a cat if he didn't talk soon. But she had to laugh at herself, because she loathed cats.

CHAPTER THREE

TALLITHA'S promotion caused a minor sensation although Miss Fortescue appeared to be unmoved by it. She congratulated Tallitha and her only other comment was that it was early days yet.

Privately, Tallitha found herself in agreement with Miss Fortescue—it was early days yet. At least, that was the only way she could describe a certain inner core of wariness she'd discovered she still felt towards her boss—wariness or confusion, it was hard to say exactly what it was . . .

And the discovery that he was conducting a long standing affair with a married woman saw her better opinion of him suffer a setback; but not only that, it confused her more.

She had wondered what Miss Fortescue had meant when she had said that he was already spoken for—in a manner of speaking—because he didn't appear to have one particular lady-love, or so Tallitha had gathered from the calls she'd put through to him from time to time.

Two weeks to the day after she had been permanently appointed, she found out. Found out that gorgeous was not an exaggeration when applied to Mrs Wentworth, who was tall and slender, beautifully dressed and groomed, had speaking violet eyes, a slightly hesitant air but lovely manners—was in fact the personification of Tallitha's idea of a classic beauty.

But there was something else about Mrs Wentworth

that Tallitha couldn't put a name to, although she tried; could only describe as a quality that made you want to rush around and open doors for her, made you want to ... well, be protective. Yes, that was it. Strange, she mused.

In fact it was the business of opening and closing doors that gave Tallitha more than an inkling of what Miles Gilmour felt for this beautiful stranger who had introduced herself to Tallitha as Mrs Wentworth, and had said that she thought Mr Gilmour was expecting her, she had rung earlier.

'Oh yes, Mrs Wentworth,' Tallitha said with a swift glance at her appointment pad, 'he is. He mentioned it a little while ago. I'll show you in.'

She knocked on the inner door and opened it. 'Mrs Wentworth, Mr Gilmour,' she murmured.

Miles Gilmour stood up immediately and glanced past Tallitha, and something in his face caught her attention, a kind of tension ...

Then Mrs Wentworth walked into his office, broke into a stumbling little run and, before Tallitha had time to close the door, she was in his waiting arms, saying his name over and over again.

Tallitha blinked and closed the door spryly, but not before she'd seen Miles Gilmour lower his dark head to kiss the mysterious Mrs Wentworth.

What have we here? she asked herself as she went slowly back to her desk and reread the note she'd made in the appointment book which said, no interruptions at all. Perhaps she's a married sister? But I don't think brothers and sisters embrace quite like that ...

It was Sonia, not surprisingly, who cleared up the mystery. She brought afternoon tea on the dot of three-thirty, just as Miles Gilmour and Mrs

Wentworth were leaving the office together, Tallitha having been instructed by her boss that he wouldn't be in for the rest of the afternoon.

'My, oh my,' Sonia said breathlessly with her eyes almost popping. 'It's on again!' she added dramatically.

'What is?'

'Mr Gilmour and Heather Wentworth!'

'Oh.' Tallitha thought for a bit. 'Is she a widow?' she enquired finally.

Sonia poured her tea and spilt a little in her eagerness to deliver herself of her precious information. 'Damn! No, she's not, Tally. It's the most heartbreaking story I ever heard,' she said dramatically and with sudden tears in her eyes. 'They were childhood sweethearts,' she said confidentially. 'Then they had a row and Mr Gilmour went overseas, and when he came back, Heather had married Hayden Wentworth, *the* Hayden Wentworth, who was years older than she was, and a right bastard by all accounts, and very, very rich of course. But it wasn't long before she realised she still loved Miles. Isn't that sad?'

'Well, yes,' Tallitha agreed. 'But it's not insoluble, is it?'

'He won't let her go! Hayden Wentworth!' Sonia's guileless blue eyes burned with reproach.

'But how can he . . .' Tallitha broke off. How can he stop her, she'd been going to say, only she thought then that it probably wasn't the discreet thing to be having this conversation with Sonia about her boss. But she found herself asking one further question out of sheer curiosity . . . 'How do you know all this, Sonia?'

'My aunt used to work here in the canteen—that's how I got the job,' she said with simple pride, then her face clouded over again. 'But that was in Mr

Gilmour's father's time when it all started, and before I was here—when it started I mean, although I did know old Mr Gilmour. But my aunt used to say that Mr Gilmour was very concerned that the only woman Mr Miles could ever love had married someone else.'

Tallitha stared at Sonia. 'Well, that's certainly awkward,' she said at last, but thinking that the whole thing sounded unreal somehow.

'It could get more awkward,' Sonia replied with unusual brevity.

'How?'

'I don't think Hayden Wentworth is the type to like his wife . . . well, you know!'

'Maybe they don't,' Tallitha said and immediately regretted it because it led to a further confidence.

'I think they did once,' Sonia whispered, going slightly pink cheeked. 'But she's so beautiful, can you blame him? Only they say Hayden came and got her back with a shotgun!'

'Oh, now . . .'

'My aunt used to reckon it could quite easily be true, Tally. And she used to know a lot of what went on. She even knew Mr Miles when he was a boy, and his sister. By the way, she's . . .'

'Sonia,' Tallitha interrupted firmly, then hesitated because she knew that Sonia would probably quite willingly die for Miles Gilmour. But all the same . . . 'Sonia, I don't think we should be discussing these . . . personal matters really, do you?'

But Sonia only chuckled. 'Everyone knows it!'

'I didn't.'

'Well you must be the only one, Tally. When you're rich and famous, see, you don't get much privacy. And Hayden Wentworth's very famous, isn't he?'

Tallitha had to admit this. Even she had heard of Hayden Wentworth—mining magnate, racehorse owner and skilled yachtsman, amongst other things.

'Anyway, better for you to know than accidentally to put your foot in it, isn't it?' Sonia said cheerfully. 'I mean you could quite easily, being his private secretary now, couldn't you? I better go—Mr Rathdowney is always dying for his afternoon tea. See you later, Tally!' she called over her shoulder as she pushed her trolley out of the office.

Tallitha didn't reply, being lost in her thoughts. Then she shook herself and got back to work.

The next day, however, she found she was still pondering Sonia's amazing revelations. Possibly because it all sounded rather far-fetched. I mean, she thought, shotguns, husbands who can't be divorced . . . the only woman he can ever love. It sounds like something out of the movies . . .

'Would you mind telling me why you're looking at me like that, Tallitha?' Miles Gilmour enquired a touch grimly.

Tallitha jumped and came out of her reverie. She was sitting opposite his desk, ostensibly taking dictation, and it was during a pause when he had consulted some figures to be quoted in the letter that she had looked curiously at his downcast head and found herself thinking of it all . . .

'Oh, no reason,' she said, but guiltily. 'How was I looking at you?'

'As if you'd never seen me before—amongst other things.'

'That's crazy,' she said with a smile.

'Then I must be going crazy,' he answered ironically.

'I didn't mean that.'

'Then I must have been imagining things. I could have sworn you were inspecting me with a distinctly critical, speculative look in your eye, like someone viewing a very odd phenomenon.'

Tallitha coloured. 'I . . . I was thinking about something else, probably, daydreaming.'

'What about?'

'I can't remember,' she lied, looking vague.

'All right, if you won't tell me, you won't.' He stopped abruptly and looked at her meditatively. 'Oh, I think I can guess,' he said softly then. 'Have you recently become privy to my affairs of the heart, Tally-ho?'

For the life of her, Tallitha couldn't prevent herself from blushing vividly.

'Who's been talking?' he shot at her, his dark blue eyes glinting.

She took a breath. 'I . . . I can't tell you that,' she said quietly, knowing she'd given herself away. 'But I didn't encourage it.' Well, I didn't really . . . 'It's none of my business,' she went on, gathering courage. 'And you can rest assured that any . . . speculation,' she flinched inwardly at this choice of word, 'will be most firmly hit on the head by—by myself.' She broke off and looked distinctly rueful for two reasons. Because she'd sounded awfully pompous and because she had had a sudden ludicrous vision of herself hitting Sonia on the head.

'That's very loyal of you, Miss Jones,' Miles Gilmour said drily. He was silent for a time. Then he said, with a tinge of mockery, 'I suppose you were trying to decide whether I was the villain of the piece or the opposite?'

Tallitha thought for a bit. 'Actually,' she said

eventually, 'I think it all sounded like the product of someone's highly fertile imagination—unbelievably dramatic, anyway.' She smiled slightly. 'And since you've prised it out of me,' she went on, 'I might as well admit that I was in the process of discounting most of it.'

Miles Gilmour stared at her narrowly. And what he said next jolted her considerably. 'I hesitate to contradict you, Tallitha, but there have been moments of high drama. Hayden Wentworth and I tend to hate each other, I'm afraid.'

She stared at him with her mouth open. Then she said uncomfortably, 'You don't . . . I really don't want to . . . I mean, it *isn't* any of my business, Mr Gilmour.'

He grinned suddenly. 'All right. But at least you've been forewarned.'

Tallitha digested this. She said blankly after a moment, 'You don't mean he's liable to come here with a . . . with a shotgun?'

'Oh, God!' Miles Gilmour said with a grin. 'Where did you hear that one?'

'I . . . Well . . . So it's not true?' Tallitha said and was amazed to hear a curious note of eagerness in her voice.

He studied her enigmatically. 'What do *you* think?' he said at last.

Tallitha opened her mouth then paused to wonder what she really did think. Was Miles Gilmour capable of wresting someone's wife away and . . . dallying with her while she was still married? Or perhaps Mrs Wentworth hadn't needed much wresting? Anyway it wasn't a very uncommon thing, was it? She looked up to find him watching her rather carefully and she coloured and muttered something unintelligible.

Which caused him to smile and say wryly, 'I do hope this hasn't come as too much of a shock to you, Tallitha. In case you hadn't noticed, I've been trying very hard to live up to your expectations.'

She coughed and her colour deepened and at the same time as she wondered whether Miles Gilmour really wasn't harder to deal with in this kind of mood than when he was in a temper, she found herself wishing she read him better because it seemed strangely important to know what the truth was. Then she bit her lip and realised he was waiting for her to reply.

'Not at all,' she said very primly, and realising it too late.

'I see it has,' he murmured with resignation and so much laughter in his eyes, she gritted her teeth.

'It has *not*,' she protested angrily. 'I told you, it's none of my business anyway, and I wish you wouldn't make fun of me like that. Because if anyone has to live up to impossible expectations, it's me!'

'Ah, but you're wrong there, Tally-ho!' he said softly. 'You're the first secretary I've apologised to in my life. But then you've had a few firsts with me, come to think of it. You're also the first woman who's come really close to scratching my eyes out.'

'If you think I'm proud of that,' Tallitha interrupted hotly, 'you're mistaken. Look, can we get on with this letter?'

They eyed each other across the desk, she mutinously and Miles Gilmour suddenly no longer laughing. 'Who was he?' he said very quietly after a moment.

'Who was who?'

'Whoever he was who frightened the life out of you once?'

'How do you . . .' She stopped abruptly.

'I never really bought the "run over by a bus" theory, Tallitha.'

She stared down at her hands and then looked rather blindly across the desk at him.

'So there was someone?'

She wouldn't, but anyway couldn't, answer.

'All right,' he said soberly at last. 'I'm sorry. You see, there I go again.' He looked at her humourlessly. 'Before you know it, you'll have completely reformed me, Miss Jones. Where was I?'

Tallitha looked back at him helplessly and then down at her pad. 'A . . . um . . . A projected annual profit margin of . . .' she said huskily.

A month passed by.

Tallitha made no drastic errors and even began to feel that she wasn't living on the edge of a precipice. I do believe I've survived the early days, she told herself, pulling a comical little face and crossing her fingers all the same.

Then the unexpected cropped up again. Or was precipitated by a car which ran her down.

It was a Friday evening and as she left work a torrential tropical downpour soaked the city, so heavy that, within a moment or two of leaving the portals of Rathdowney House, she was soaked to the skin and gasping at the force of the rain. A huge black cloud hovered above, turning the daylight to heavy dusk, and great claps of thunder and forks of vivid lightning tore the heavens asunder.

Tallitha winced and shivered, forcibly restraining herself from cowering in public because she hated lightning and thunder, and on a stupid impulse dashed across the street against the light with every intention of diving into a café she knew until it was over.

But while the street had looked clear to cross, a sleek grey car had materialised out of the firm's underground garage, and before she could even think of taking evasive action its low front bumper had grazed the back of her legs and bowled her over into the gutter.

There was a squeal of tyres and the slamming of a door, and then Miles Gilmour was leaning over her, cursing angrily. I'd know those curses anywhere, she thought dazedly, as she tried to sit up.

But it seemed she was not so immediately recognisable because it was only after a minute or so of delivering himself of his pungent sentiments on people who crossed streets against the lights, in the middle of a bloody storm, too, that he stopped and said incredulously, 'Tallitha?'

'Yes. Yes, it's me,' she managed to get out. 'I'm sorry.'

He was kneeling down beside her in the gutter, soaking wet now himself, and a small crowd of hardy souls had gathered. 'Are you all right?' he asked sharply.

'I think so,' she said huskily, but knew she was not for she couldn't stop shaking, from shock probably, and one ankle that was doubled up beneath her ached ferociously.

'No you're not, you little idiot,' Miles Gilmour said angrily.

'Fair go, mate,' a voice from the crowd remonstrated. 'You could have killed her!'

'Well, I didn't,' Miles replied shortly. 'Give me a hand, will you?'

It was with the aid of many hands that she was carefully put into Miles Gilmour's car, and he drove off. 'W-where are we going to?' she whispered.

'The hospital,' he said briefly. 'Don't talk.'

'No . . . no, I'm sure I don't need to go to the hospital,' she stammered. 'I think I've only sprained my ankle. Please, you don't need to . . .'

'All the same, I am,' he said curtly, then deliberately softened his voice. 'Relax if you can, Tally-ho!'

She subsided miserably because she really was feeling ill and sore, but if anything the thought of taking him out of his way was making her feel worse.

'Y-you don't have to stay,' she said then. 'I can get a taxi home. Besides, I really don't think there's anything seriously wrong with me.'

They'd pulled up at a traffic light and through the gloom the car was filled with the pinkish glow of it. Miles Gilmour turned his head and surveyed her. 'You're a very determined little person, aren't you, Tallitha Jones?' he said softly. 'But I feel bad enough as it is. So I'll be staying until they check you over thoroughly and then I'll be taking you home if they agree, and nothing you can say will stop me. Right?'

She swallowed and foolish tears began to trickle down her cheeks. 'It wasn't your fault . . .'

'That's true, but . . .'

'So you don't have to feel bad!'

'I can assure you one *always* feels bad after shouting and swearing at someone who is hurt!'

'But . . .'

'Will you shut up, Miss Jones?' he commanded with a grin and put the car into gear as the lights changed. But before they moved off he took one of her hands into his and pressed it gently.

Which was curiously comforting.

Several hours later Miles Gilmour looked round her bedsitter with a little smile and said, 'It suits you.'

'I'm only an amateur decorator.'

'Then you've done well for an amateur. Right, who are these people I'm to ring?'

'Oh! Oh, I'll do it!' Tallitha said anxiously from the bed where he had deposited her carefully after carrying her in from the car. She had one ankle tightly strapped, a livid bruise darkening on her cheekbone and an assortment of other bruises and scrapes, some not visible beneath her dirty and torn clothes. Other than that, according to the hospital, she was only suffering from mild shock.

'Well, I don't quite see how,' Miles Gilmour murmured, looking around again. 'There's not even a telephone here. Is it in the kitchen?'

'No, but . . .' She flushed uncomfortably.

'Tallitha.' He walked over to the bed and sat down beside her. 'Were you lying at the hospital?' he asked a little grimly.

She bit her lip and tried to look away but he caught her chin. 'Tell me,' he insisted.

'I'll . . . I'll be all right,' she whispered. 'They said there was nothing wrong with me.'

'They *said*,' he interrupted, 'that they would release you if you had someone to look after you because you wouldn't be able to get about on that ankle for a few days, and because you needed complete rest to get over the shock. *You* said there *was* someone. Why did you lie? There isn't anyone, is there?'

'Yes there is! There's a house full of people here! You see, it's divided into four flats, this house. And there's always someone around.'

'Tell me their names then and I'll go and knock someone up.' He released her chin looking slightly mollified.

'Well I don't know their names, but . . .'

Her flustered words faded into silence and she looked away because Miles Gilmour was staring at her with a mixture of impatience and compassion.

'You mean,' he said quietly, 'there's a house full of strangers. Only it's more, isn't it?' he added acutely. 'It's a world full of strangers, isn't it? Why?'

Tallitha opened her mouth then closed her eyes. 'Why?' she said equally quietly. 'Because that's the way I want it, so you don't have to feel sorry for me. In fact I wish you'd just leave me alone now. I can manage. They did give me a pair of crutches.'

'No,' he said at last, 'I can't do that. It will have to be one of the strangers.' And he got up and walked out.

But he was back about ten minutes later with an extremely surprised-looking blonde girl of about Tallitha's age.

'Mrs Martin here,' he said, 'lives next door to you, Tallitha. She's volunteered to keep an eye on you and she'll help you to bed. This is Tallitha Jones, Mrs Martin . . .'

'Call me Diana,' the girl said quickly. 'Actually I've lived in the next-door flat for a month or so now and I've wanted to get to know you but you seemed to prefer to keep to yourself. I thought my baby might have bothered you, perhaps. She sometimes cries at night. Sorry,' she said with an embarrassed little shrug.

Tallitha stared at her. 'Yes. I mean, no,' she said finally. 'I've heard it but it hasn't bothered me. I . . .'

'Oh good!' Diana Martin said eagerly, but her expression turned to one of concern. 'You are in a mess,' she said anxiously. 'But never mind, I'll give you a hand. Don't you worry,' she added, turning to Miles, 'I'll look after her and I've got your phone number. There's a phone box just down the road.'

'That's settled then,' Miles Gilmour said, looking directly at Tallitha. 'If you need anything, don't hesitate to call. Good night, Tally-ho.'

He left without waiting for a reply.

'What a gorgeous man!' Diana Martin said tentatively. 'Wish I had a boss like that, even if he did run me over, but then I'm out of the workforce at the moment . . . Actually,' she took a deep breath and said in a rush, 'I'm not even *Mrs* Martin. I'm not married. Thought that might have—well, put you off, too, because it's pretty obvious I don't have a husband and some people, well, some people . . .' She broke off and stared at Tallitha worriedly.

'No.' Tallitha said, rubbing her face distractedly and with the glitter of tears in her green eyes, 'I'm not one of those, Diana,' she said huskily. 'I'm very glad to know you. It's just that I've lived on my own for so long now, I think I've got out of the habit of knowing how to mix with people.'

Sunday saw Tallitha feeling a lot better and she spent most of the afternoon up with the aid of the crutches the hospital had supplied, but by five o'clock, Diana Martin had ordered her back to bed and brought her baby into her to keep her company while she went out to get some milk and bread.

And that was how Miles Gilmour found her—in a pretty pink nightgown, propped up against her frilly pillows with Diana's baby lying in the crook of her arm—when he arrived quite unexpectedly. In fact she'd been trying to make the baby smile, unsuccessfully, and it was a rueful but tender, laughing face she lifted to call 'come in' at his knock, thinking it must be Diana.

'Well,' he said, with lifted eyebrows, 'you do look better.'

'Oh!' Tallitha started. 'It's you,' she said.

'Mmm,' he agreed and closed the door behind him. 'It is indeed I.' He shot her an amused look and set a basket of oranges and a packet down beside her alarm clock. 'And I guess this is the baby that cries in the night? Baby Martin?'

'Yes. I ... I didn't expect you. I mean, you didn't have to come,' Tallitha said confusedly.

'So you gave me to understand,' he replied, and added mildly, 'I have a reputation for doing things people tell me not to. I thought you might have discovered that by now.'

He looked around and swung her basket chair round to face the bed, and sat down as if he was perfectly at home. He wore crisp white trousers, a sky blue open-necked sports shirt and canvas loafers. His dark hair was ruffled and windblown and Tallitha found herself thinking it was the first time she'd seen him informally dressed and that he looked bigger, but younger.

'I ...'

'How ...'

'You go first,' he said politely.

'No, it was nothing.' She coloured and tried to sit up.

'Here,' he said, 'allow me.' And he leant forward and removed the baby and sat back with it in the crook of his arm as if nursing babies was something he did every day of his life. In fact the infant stared up at him with cross-eyed intensity for a moment, then smiled a blinding smile revealing rosy pink, perfectly toothless gums.

'Well!' Tallitha was moved to say a touch indignantly. 'She wouldn't do that for me.'

'I have a way with babies,' he remarked casually, straightening the infant's singlet deftly.

'How come?' Tallitha couldn't resist asking.

'I got thrown in at the deep end once, I suppose you could say,' he replied with a grin. 'My sister had twin babies and one day when I was visiting her she got a call to say that her oldest kid at a tennis coaching class had fallen and broken his arm. She dropped everything and said, "Miles, you're in charge." It took me two hours of nerve-racking yelling from them before I discovered the key—a firm but gentle hand and a firm voice. I read aloud to them from the *Wall Street Journal*—a back number. My brother-in-law Rupert is a financier. It was amazing how quickly it sent them to sleep,' he said, perfectly seriously.

'You . . . you're having me on,' she said, but finding it hard not to laugh.

'Not at all. Look.'

She looked and was amazed to see that the baby was dozing peacefully, for all that it was due for a feed shortly and, according to its mother anyway, *never* slept in late afternoon.

'I'm surprised someone hasn't dragged you to the altar for your fatherly abilities if nothing else,' Tallitha said humorously.

'Oh, I don't think I'd be a good marital bet somehow,' he said after a moment's thought and on a suddenly dry note.

'Not . . . ever?' Tallitha asked, and wished immediately that she hadn't.

But he looked amused again. 'I have enough trouble finding secretaries. Can you imagine how hard it would be for me to find a suitable wife?'

'Especially if your affections are already spoken for.' Did I say that? Tallitha thought, and closed her eyes in a hot flood of embarrassment because she had said it. Incredibly, the words had simply escaped, echoed her thoughts which had conjured up a sudden vision of Heather Wentworth.

She opened her eyes to see him staring at her with his mouth set and a shadow in those dark blue eyes. Of anger? she wondered miserably. It *isn't* any of my business. 'I'm sorry,' she whispered. 'I shouldn't have said that.'

'Why not?' he countered. 'Unfortunately it's all too true.' His voice was hard and she shivered.

'Couldn't she—I mean, if you love each other and it was a mistake, her marrying Hayden Wentworth— couldn't she divorce him?'

'It seems not. When you're a MacPherson you don't go back on your word.'

Tallitha's mouth dropped open. '*She's* a MacPherson? Mrs Wentworth?'

'Yes. Didn't you know?'

'No.'

'You seem to know most other things,' he said a shade cynically.

'That's only because . . .' Tallitha began to say with some spirit, but she winced inwardly and made herself change tack. 'As a matter of fact I was beginning to think of the MacPhersons as a lost tribe—rather like the McIntyres nearly became!' She hesitated as her attempt at humour fell flat, and found herself feeling guilty and uncertain. 'I'm sorry,' she said then. 'I didn't mean to be inquisitive. The thing is,' she smiled perplexedly, 'seeing you sitting there with that baby—well, somehow it seems as if you're just an ordinary person.' She glanced at him to see if he understood.

He said, 'I am.'

'But I mean not my boss.' She shrugged and added, 'I don't suppose it makes much sense.'

'Curiously it does, Tallitha,' Miles Gilmour said after a while. 'It's only a pity,' he went on slowly, 'that you won't allow me to return the compliment.'

'I don't understand.'

'Well, put it this way, you're not *only* my secretary. Not a robot, but a living, breathing ordinary person, too. Addicted to oranges perhaps,' his eyes laughed at her, 'sometimes accident-prone, but . . .' He stopped and then their gazes caught and held. 'But like me you obviously have some problems.'

The silence that followed was broken only by the baby sucking its lips. Then the door opened and Diana waltzed in saying, '*Sorry* I was so long but the first shop was out of bread and I had to . . . Oh! Mr Gilmour!' Her blue eyes widened even more at the sight of her baby in his arms. 'Oh my! And she's asleep,' she said incredulously.

'Well, I think she's about to wake up,' Miles said to her with his most charming smile. 'With thoughts of nourishment on her mind by the sound of it. I'm afraid I'm quite useless in that department.' He handed the baby over and Diana laughed heartily. 'What's her name?' he asked. 'By the way, she looks a lot like you,' he added, further endearing himself to Diana who was obviously smitten anyway.

'Amanda. Do you really think so?'

'Definitely.'

'I thought she looked like . . .' Diana broke off and shrugged. 'Anyway,' she added brightly, too brightly, 'I'll take her away and feed her and leave you two to talk. Give me a knock when you leave and I'll make Tallitha some supper. 'Bye!'

Miles closed the door behind her. 'An unmarried mother, I gather,' he said soberly.

'Yes. Her . . . the father walked out on her when she

discovered she was pregnant. She's quite sure she can go it alone, but . . .' She shrugged.

'You don't think she can?'

'Yes, I think she will,' Tallitha said after a moment. 'But I don't envy her.'

'When I first came in,' Miles Gilmour said, 'I got the distinct impression you did. You looked—different somehow. Alive and loving.'

'Babies probably do that to you in the short term.'

'Ever had one of your own?'

Tallitha stared at him with parted lips and stunned eyes. 'Whatever made you think that?' she whispered.

'I don't know.' He wandered over to Mason's cage and stood looking at the bird with his hands shoved into his pocket. 'I guess I'm working without a script, which is where you have the advantage over me. Like a drink?'

Tallitha blinked. 'I haven't got anything.'

'Ah, but I have.' He returned to the bed and opened the brown paper packet to reveal a bottle of brandy. 'I always take brandy to the sick. It's renowned for its medicinal qualities, isn't it?' He strolled into the kitchen and reappeared with two tumblers and some ice. 'Brandy on the rocks.' He poured it and handed her a glass which she took because she couldn't think what else to do.

'Cheers, Tally-ho!' he said sitting down again. 'But I haven't asked you how you are? Physically, I mean.'

'I . . . I'm feeling much better,' she said dazedly. 'I'll probably be able to come into work tomorrow if you don't mind me hobbling around.'

'I most certainly do.'

'Oh? Why?'

'Because I've already spent time explaining you away, Tally-ho,' he said. 'But I can't blame my non-existent cat this time, can I?'

'I . . . You ran *me* over!'

'Which makes us quits, don't you think? Although, if we're to be perfectly precise, I do feel I was the innocent party on both . . . Don't throw your drink at me, my dear.'

'You . . . you're . . .' Tallitha surveyed his laughing eyes furiously, then she looked at the glass she'd raised aloft and for the life of her she couldn't help lowering it and giggling suddenly. 'You're impossible!'

'No. I'm not.'

'Well, a bit mad then. I didn't know bosses could be like this,' she said wryly.

'Mad?'

'So nice . . .' She looked suddenly self-conscious and they drank in silence for a while.

Until he said, 'You're not going to respond, I gather.'

She didn't pretend to misunderstand him. 'I don't really have any problems,' she said quietly. 'Just some memories that catch me unawares sometimes.' She looked at her glass a little owlishly. Brandy on the rocks was not something she had much experience of. 'But I think to love someone must be very special and . . . and that there should be a solution. For you.'

'That sounds very romantic.'

She shrugged. 'Perhaps. It doesn't seem to happen very often. Not to love someone really.'

'Are you talking from experience?' he queried quietly.

'I'm talking from having seen you together. Only for a moment or two, before I closed the door.'

'Perhaps appearances—before you close the door—can be deceptive.'

They stared at each other, he dispassionately, she burningly, for a long, long moment. Then she put her glass down and said tonelessly, 'Perhaps. There I go again. You see, though, you're as reluctant to talk about it really as I . . .' She stopped.

'Well, at least that's an admission that all is not well in the house of Jones,' he said wryly.

'*In vino veritas,*' Tallitha murmured. 'I'm sure if I was in hospital they'd have thrown you out for bringing alcohol on to the premises.'

'I do it more cunningly in hospitals.'

'I'm sure you do,' Tallitha said with a tiny smile. 'And I don't suppose you've ever been thrown out of anywhere in your life.'

'Have you?'

'Yes, once,' she said musingly. 'But perhaps it was the best thing that ever happened to me in the long term.'

He looked at her curiously. 'I can't imagine you pinching the silver.'

'Oh, it was something much more precious.' She was silent for a time, then she picked up her glass and sipped at it. 'You know, I do feel a lot better. I really could come to work tomorrow. How will you cope otherwise?'

'I won't even try.'

'That's what I'm afraid of!' She raised her eyes heavenwards.

He laughed, but said, 'No. Give it a few days. I'll try not to get things too disorganised. And in the meantime,' he drained his glass and stood up, 'I ought to get going. By the way, I've been meaning to ask you something. Who's Mason?'

Tallitha grimaced and pointed. 'My bird. He won't talk.'

'Oh! I see. Perhaps you aren't teaching him the right words?'

'Yes I am. He's just stubborn.'

'I wonder who he gets that from?' Miles Gilmour said innocently and, greatly to her surprise, leant down and kissed her cheek just below the bruise on it. 'Keep getting better, Miss Jones,' he said with a wicked grin. 'I need you!'

And he was gone, leaving Tallitha with her lips parted, her cheeks flushed, and a curious look of bewilderment in her green eyes.

Diana found her sitting in the same position some time later and asked her if something was wrong.

'No!' Tallitha said, coming out of her reverie with an effort. 'Nothing. Would you like a drink?'

Diana would love a drink, she said, with a sudden sparkle in her eyes. But she fetched some ginger ale from her flat to dilute the brandy and in fact they had two drinks each, scrambled eggs for supper and played a hilarious game of Scrabble until bedtime.

'Now that's what I call something useful to bring to the sick,' Diana said dreamily.

And perhaps it was the brandy but she suddenly started to cry.

'Tell me,' Tallitha said softly.

Diana did, beyond the brief outline she'd already given her. And Tallitha had tears in her eyes, too, because not only had Amanada's father abandoned Diana but her parents had, too. Unfortunately, as it turned out, she'd been an only child and the apple of her father's eye—a very strong, dominating man, apparently. And when he'd discovered his daughter's predicament, he'd accused her of wasting her life, throwing it away, and of being a cheap slut into the bargain.

'I couldn't stand it. I couldn't stay,' Diana wept. 'He was so angry and so disappointed. Every time he looked at me, I knew what he was thinking—it went on for months. So I left before the baby was born. I had some money saved and I applied for state help. When she was born I wrote to Mum, but he wouldn't even let her come and see me ... I still write to her sometimes because I know he's giving her a hard time, too. He ... I always knew he could be hard, but not this hard.'

Tallitha had said nothing—what could one say? But they'd sat for a while in a sad but companionable silence. And finally Diana had brightened up and smiled her old smile.

'I think I needed to tell someone,' she said. 'I feel a lot better. Thanks.'

And she'd gone off to bed, leaving Tallitha marvelling a little at her indomitability. And then, prey again to the thoughts she'd been entertaining before Diana had joined her for supper.

She switched off her lamp and lay in the darkness wondering about Miles Gilmour and Heather Wentworth. Was she wrong in thinking he really loved Hayden Wentworth's beautiful wife? And how much of Sonia's gossip was true?

'But why does it matter to me?' she murmured aloud restlessly. 'If he is—If they *are* it means nothing to me. Only it does, because I'd like to think he wasn't—Oh, God! Am I becoming another Sonia? Determined to think that the sun shines out of Miles Gilmour? Not that Sonia seemed to mind about Heather Wentworth. But I ... seem to. And I also seem to mind that he can't have her if he really loves her. How curious. Perhaps I'm on the road to becoming one of those devoted private secretaries. Who would have thought it? Especially devoted to Miles Gilmour ...'

CHAPTER FOUR

TALLITHA returned to work three days later. Her visible bruises had faded to the point where she could conceal them with a make-up stick—which struck her as ironic—and Miles Gilmour had contrived, God knows how, she thought, not to get into too much of a mess. She discovered later that Miss Fortescue herself had taken command.

Her ankle was still sore on occasions but she could get around without the crutches and only a slight suggestion of a limp.

But it was quite plain to her that her boss was not in a good mood from the moment she stepped over the threshold, although he greeted her with a grin. But there was something in those dark blue eyes that alerted her—a glitter of some emotion suppressed. And she thought how far removed he looked, in his charcoal suit, grey pin-striped shirt and maroon silk tie, from the Miles Gilmour who had visited her. It was almost as if there were only one point in common between the two images she now had of him—his smile. But as they day progressed, she rarely even saw that.

She also discovered that one quite significant change had occurred during her time off. Not really a change, but an addition to the hierarchy of Rathdowney, MacPherson & Gilmour, in the person of Leicester Rathdowney, son of Hugo. In fact that was how he introduced himself to Tallitha after wandering into her office mid-morning.

'Oh. How do you do?' Tallitha said politely.

'Very well, thank you. By the way, people call me Les, it's simpler,' Leicester Rathdowney replied, looking her over in the manner a very experienced bloodstock agent would a filly, although he was only about twenty-eight or nine, she judged. He was also very slim but quite tall, fair but brown-eyed, and tailored exquisitely.

'So you're the mystery lady,' he went on, finally releasing her hand.

Tallitha looked surprised. 'There's no mystery about me, Mr Rathdowney,' she murmured. 'I've been sick, that's all.'

'Please call me Les,' he said plaintively. 'Everyone does. And I hear you have quite a temper. I must say I adore fiery women, especially ones with lovely red hair and green eyes, not to mention . . .'

Two things happened simultaneously at that point. Tallitha sat down behind her desk hurriedly and the door to the inner office clicked open.

'Well, Les,' Miles Gilmour remarked as he strolled through, 'I see you've introduced yourself to my secretary.'

'I have, Miles, I have,' the younger man said. 'And I was just telling her that someone mentioned she had a fiery temper. I must say you should have a lively time between the two of you!'

Miles Gilmour glanced at Tallitha with narrowed eyes and she bit her lip and wondered, not for the first time, how she could have done what she had. Or whether she'd ever be allowed to forget it. And at the same time she spared some uncharitable thoughts towards Mr Rathdowney senior, who had obviously passed the news on to his son.

But it seemed her boss was not prepared to

comment on her temper—or his—because he said abruptly, 'Were you looking for me, Les?'

'Was I? I can't remember . . . Oh yes! If you recall, I'm supposed to be familiarising myself with your end of the operation.' There was a slightly sardonic note detectable in his voice, and Tallitha intercepted a glance between the two men which left her in no doubt that they didn't like each other.

But Miles said expressionlessly, 'Then I'll take you along to Jeff Seymour, my second-in-command. He'll probably find plenty for you to do.'

Opinions were divided in the canteen that day. Some of the girls thought Hugo Rathdowney's son was a real card, others that he was rather creepy—good-looking, yes, but . . .

Some more salient points did emerge about him, though. That he'd been managing a branch office out west for some time, and that he'd handled the sales of a couple of million-dollar stations—a feather in his cap. And that he'd been brought in . . . Well, there again, opinions were divided. As a natural progression in his career, or to spike the guns of Miles Gilmour? After all, he was sole heir to Hugo Rathdowney.

'Guess what, Tallitha?' Sonia said at teatime, lowering her voice mysteriously.

'What?' Tallitha looked up, fully expecting more on the subject of Les Rathdowney.

'Heather Wentworth is going to have a baby!'

'Are you sure?'

'Of course. There was a report in the paper. She was in hospital for some tests. And because there was speculation, Hayden Wentworth announced it officially.'

Tallitha closed her eyes briefly.

'Must say he's taken it very well, hasn't he?' Sonia
said then.

No he hasn't, Tallitha thought. So that's it . . .

'But what happened to you?' Sonia enquired. 'I
asked Mr Gilmour and he said you had a freak
accident.'

'I suppose I did.'

'Watch out for the new Mr Rathdowney,' Sonia
said, lowering her voice again dramatically. 'Like his
dad, he is. Not that Mr Hugo . . . I mean, he's an old
sweetie, really, isn't he?'

Fortunately she didn't wait for an answer but
pushed her trolley out with a gay wave.

But as it turned out her warning wasn't untimely.
Because, although Les Rathdowney had been con-
signed to Mr Seymour's care, he found plenty of
opportunity to visit Tallitha's office and was clever
enough always to have a genuine excuse—or so it
seemed. In fact it became quite a talking point among
the girls downstairs—how taken he was with Tallitha
Jones.

Short of being deliberately rude or losing her
temper, which she was extremely loath to do, Tallitha
found it hard to get across to him that she found his
curiously hot brown eyes repulsive, his never-ending,
thinly veiled remarks about the attractiveness of her
person extremely unwelcome, and his equally thinly
disguised desire to touch her whenever possible
actually nauseating.

Keep cool and calm and simply ignore him when
possible, she advised herself. He's got to get the
message sooner or later. I'm sure that's how the other
private secretaries would treat him, she mused. But of
course all the other private secretaries were quite a bit
older than she was and for that matter older than

Leicester Rathdowney. Maybe he'll develop a passion for an older woman? she pondered with a spark of humour.

That Miles Gilmour was even aware of what was going on didn't dawn on her until he strode in from lunch one day, found Les sitting on her desk and ordered him out curtly.

'I only came to deliver these figures, Miles!' Les said reproachfully.

'How long does it take to deliver a few sheets of paper? And since when were you the office boy?' Miles demanded, his blue eyes hard and glinting.

'I'm going, I'm going.'

'And close the door behind you!'

'He ...' Tallitha began but Miles Gilmour turned on her as the door closed and said coldly, 'I wouldn't encourage him if I were you, Tallitha. Apart from wasting *my* time, he's the last person for a girl like you.'

Tallitha gasped. 'I wasn't ...'

'You mean you weren't sitting there drinking in his compliments about how your blouse matches your eyes and what shapely legs you've got? I heard it!'

'No. I wasn't! I mean I wasn't drinking it in,' she protested angrily. 'And what do you mean—a girl like me?'

'Oh, don't give me that!' he said impatiently. 'You know exactly what I mean.'

'No I don't!' she cried. 'You make me sound like a girl who keels over for any man who pays her a compliment!'

'I don't mean that at all, as you very well know. I mean, for a girl who's been hurt ... But perhaps you've changed? You don't seem to be repulsing him.'

Tallitha stared at him, almost speechless with anger.

'Look,' she said through her teeth, 'I am repulsing him, the best way I know how. I'm trying to ignore him and stay calm. What else would you like me to do?'

'Try scratching his eyes out,' Miles Gilmour replied sardonically. 'I can guarantee he'd get the message then.' He stormed into his office and slammed the door, leaving Tallitha scarlet in the face and angry enough to fully justify her ill-gotten reputation.

'I hate you, Miles Gilmour,' she whispered, and burst into tears.

The inner door opened. 'Oh, I had an idea you'd be crying,' he said drily, leaning his shoulders against the door frame.

'I hate you,' she whispered again and turned away, valiantly trying to stem the tears.

He didn't say anything for a while, just watched her slim shoulders shaking. Then he walked over and sat on the desk himself. 'Here,' he said.

She turned back reluctantly to see him holding out his handkerchief. 'I've got my own somewhere.' But a hunt through her skirt pockets failed to reveal it.

'I'll do it myself in a moment,' he warned, and she knew he was quite capable of wiping her eyes and nose for her so she snatched his handkerchief and did the job herself. Then balled it up and put it in her pocket. 'You'll have to go without one for the rest of the day,' she muttered beneath her breath.

'Serve me right, won't it?'

She set her teeth. 'If you dare laugh at me after . . . after saying what you did I'll walk out of here and never come back,' she threatened. 'I *wasn't* encouraging him. Quite frankly I detest him, but he is— I don't know what his official capacity is, but he *is* a Rathdowney.'

Miles Gilmour's lips twitched but he forebore to laugh. 'For that matter, I'm a Gilmour,' he said.

Tallitha looked at him with some tears still sparkling on her lashes. 'I don't see what that's got to do with it.' But as soon as she'd said it, she was conscious of having fallen into a trap.

'Well, you never allow that to intimidate you. You've just told me you hate me.' His eyes glinted wickedly.

Tallitha opened her mouth and shut it as the logic of this struck her rather forcibly. She coloured and looked away awkwardly. 'We . . . we seem to have got to know each other quite well,' she said helplessly.

'Despite your best efforts,' he agreed wryly. Then he sobered as she looked intolerably confused. 'Tallitha, Les has no official capacity yet. He's here to learn the ropes, *not* to make any girl's life a misery. Tell him to get lost in no uncertain terms, and if he gives you any more trouble, tell me. But in point of fact, whatever his capacity you shouldn't have to put up with that kind of nonsense.'

She considered this then tilted her chin. 'You're right.' She smiled faintly. 'I thought I was handling him as a . . . as a private secretary should,' she said ruefully. 'In a mature, sophisticated manner.' She grimaced. 'Sorry.'

He said, with a smile lurking in his eyes, 'If I'd wanted a mature, sophisticated secretary, I'd have got myself one, so for God's sake don't try to change yourself. How's Diana? And the baby?'

'Oh, fine! She's sitting up now.'

'Do you have much to do with her?'

'Yes,' Tallitha confessed. 'I babysit for her often on the weekends. It gives Diana a break. And sometimes we all go out together. We took her to the park last

Sunday. She loved being out. I guess,' she said a little diffidently, 'I have to thank you for introducing me to Diana.'

'Well,' his eyes danced, 'give me time and I might be able to go one better.'

'What do you mean?'

'I might even come up with a nice young man for you!'

Curiously, over the next couple of weeks, she didn't get the opportunity to tell Les Rathdowney to get lost because he stopped pestering her all of his own accord. In fact he went out of his way to ignore her. Perhaps Miles got the message across that day, she thought. Or perhaps he said something to him afterwards? Not that she really minded how it happened!

As for Miles Gilmour himself, there were certain signs, some more visible to his secretary than anyone else, that he was both living and working at a frenetic pace. She noticed his picture in the social pages several times, at different parties with different women. Of course it was getting close to Christmas and therefore, traditionally, party time.

But then she was also receiving calls for him from mysterious women—more than he'd ever had. After putting some through to him, however, she learnt that particular lesson the hard way.

'Tallitha, what the hell do you think you're paid to do?' he enquired one day after one such call, striding into her office with his face set and angry.

She blinked. 'I don't know what you mean.'

'I mean, will you stop putting these personal calls through to me, damn it! I'm far too busy for them!'

'W-well, what shall I say?' she stammered.

'Anything! I don't care . . . whatever private bloody

secretaries say! You must be able to think of something since you're so concerned with becoming a mature, sophisticated one,' he said sarcastically.

The unfairness of this gibe all but took her breath away. The overall unfairness also struck her, so that she longed to say, you're only using these women to help you forget that Heather Wentworth is more than ever tied to her husband now . . .

But of course she didn't say it—for two reasons. Firstly, because of a vow she'd made never to comment on it again after being unforgivably forward on the subject—admittedly under the influence of brandy on the rocks, but all the same . . .

And secondly, because he didn't give her a chance. 'Tell 'em I've gone to the back of Bourke!' he commanded, and stalked back to his office, slamming the door.

Tallitha sighed. You poor door, she thought. Then it dawned on her that, although her boss was exhibiting classic symptoms of his own, peculiar, high-handed unreasonableness, she couldn't find it in her heart to be angry or hurt. She pondered this for a while and decided again, with a curious little trip in her heartbeat, that she was concerned about Miles Gilmour, she just couldn't help it.

Which was probably why she firmly pushed aside her thoughts on how unfair he was being to all those other women, and developed an equally firm formula for dealing with them.

As for work, the company was developing an urban shopping centre—a new departure for Rathdowney, MacPherson & Gilmour still in the planning stages—but the flood of work it entailed, calling for tenders, contracts and sub-contracts, leasing arrangements, finance, etc., all were Miles Gilmour's final re-

sponsibility and in consequence both he and Tallitha
were flat out.

But at least I'm leading a peaceful life otherwise, she
reflected once, and jumped as the phone from the
inner office was slammed down. On, she knew, the
legal firm which was responsible for drawing up all the
contracts and had apparently botched up some.

She waited a moment or two and then took several
recently received Telexes into him.

He was lying back in his chair with his eyes closed
and he didn't stir. His tie was loosened and the neck of
his shirt unbuttoned, and there were lines of pain and
weariness etched into his face.

Tallitha put the pieces of paper down on his desk
and walked over quietly to draw the curtains against
the bright afternoon sunlight. Then she went into his
bathroom and reappeared with two aspirins and a glass
of water.

'Mr Gilmour?' she murmured, standing right beside
him.

His eyes fluttered open and he stared up at her for a
moment, then sat up and took the aspirins.

'How did you know?' He swallowed them down
with the water and lay back again.

'My mother used to get splitting headaches
sometimes.'

'Splitting—how accurate,' he said, his lips barely
moving.

'Why don't you go home?' she suggested. 'You're
. . . I think you've been trying to do too much.'

A faint grin curved his lips. 'You sound positively
maternal, Tallitha . . . But perhaps you're right.' He
grimaced.

'I can hold everyone off for the rest of the
afternoon.'

Those heavy eyelids lifted and he watched her for a while in silence. 'I like that dress, by the way,' he said finally.

'Thanks. It's new.' She looked down at the latest addition to her wardrobe—a two-piece outfit, but matching so that it looked like one but could be mixed and matched. It was a blouse and a very full skirt in a creamy cotton with trims of sage green around the neck and the bottom of the skirt and a green, wide, soft belt that emphasised her slim waist. She wore green open-toed shoes with slender heels, and a chunky green and cream striped bangle. And her hair was up in a knot on the top of her head, as she usually wore it to work, and, as usually happened to it, with some feathery curls escaping.

'You know what I'd really like to do,' he said then, still watching her. 'I'd like to go away to the beach for a month and hide. Care to come with me?'

'Why don't you? For a few days?'

'Does that mean yes or no?'

Her lips trembled into a smile and she sketched a curtsy. She said gravely, however, 'No. You need perfect peace and quiet for a splitting headache. Anyway, who would hold the multitudes off if we both disappeared?'

'Why do I get the feeling you're humouring me, Tallitha?' he asked ruefully. 'I quite thought I'd shock you rigid with that invitation.'

'I'm not shockable any more,' she replied equally ruefully. 'Working for you must have done it.' Her green eyes glimmered mischievously. 'But no, seriously, why don't you go home? I won't let the place fall to pieces, I promise.'

He sat up and thrust a hand wearily through his hair.

She waited with bated breath, almost, and an indecipherable emotion which she suddenly realised with a stinging sense of shock was a feeling of tenderness towards him.

She moved restlessly at the same time as he said abruptly, 'All right, I will. Seeing as you've become so expert a private secretary, Miss Jones,' he said with a lurking smile, 'I'll take your advice.'

He reached for his jacket and slung it over his arm, but stood for a moment with his hands shoved into his pockets, surveying her in the dim light.

Then he moved round the desk to where she stood. 'You're also very sweet, Tally-ho,' he said softly and kissed her brow lightly. 'See you tomorrow—I hope restored and fighting . . . Rather, make that fit, plain fit.'

Tallitha stared after him long after he'd gone from view, and her eyes were curiously confused.

The question of the company Christmas party caused Tallitha some heart-searching. Each staff member received a formal invitation for self *and* partner, and it was a dinner dance to be held in the canteen. It was Sonia's duty to collect the replies, which were supposed to be in four days before the event, to assist catering. Tallitha had discussed the invitation with Diana, who had become avidly interested in everything that went on at Rathdowney, MacPherson & Gilmour, and had expressed a reluctance to go.

'But of course you must go!' Diana had said, quite shocked.

'Who with? That's the problem.'

'I'm sure you don't have to have a partner!'

'I'd prefer not to be a wallflower.'

'Oh, of course you won't! Mr Gilmour for one wouldn't let you be!'

Diana had decided that Miles Gilmour, as well as being gorgeous, was also the embodiment of every virtue known to woman and, Tallitha suspected, didn't really believe her when she said he wasn't that easy to work for. But then Diana, who Tallitha had grown to be very fond of, surprised her sometimes with her naïve outlook on life. You'd think after what she has been through she'd be the embodiment of cynicism, Tallitha had reflected a couple of times. As I am . . .?

But it was Sonia who decided the issue. 'Not come?' she said with a horrified look. 'Oh, you can't do that— unless you're dying!'

Tallitha had to smile.

'No, it's true!' Sonia insisted. 'Mr Rathdowney likes everyone to come.'

'Well the thing is, Sonia,' Tallitha said honestly, 'I don't have a partner.'

'Oh, that doesn't matter! Quite a lot of us don't— you don't *have* to bring one. Actually I sometimes think it's better not to, unless you want him to be picked to pieces by some of the catty bitches who work here.' A fleeting look of hurt flitted across her pretty face and Tallitha winced inwardly for her.

'Are you bringing someone this year, Sonia?' she asked.

'Yes, I am,' Sonia said after a moment. 'You can sit with us if you like . . . I mean, you don't have to, but . . .'

'I'd like to very much,' Tallitha said.

Deciding what to wear was the next hurdle, and she gathered from the excited talk among the girls that it was exercising quite a few minds. But, a little to Diana's disappointment, Tallitha would be shopping for something simple, she said. What she finally found was a slightly A-line, loose shift in a coppery taffeta with narrow shoulder straps. The top of the bodice, the only part of the dress that was fitted, hugged her figure perfectly and had three narrow tiers of a more golden taffeta stitched to it.

'Well,' Diana said, circling Tallitha critically the night she bought it, 'I thought you said you were getting something simple!'

'But it is! Isn't it . . .?'

'It's the most simply elegant dress I've seen for years! Who would have thought the copper and the gold would go so well? Or suit you so well! It makes your eyes greener than ever. You know what you need? You have the right neck for it—wear a brown velvet ribbon round your neck with a cameo. That would just give it the perfect touch!'

'I haven't got a cameo.'

'Well, we'll find something,' Diana said confidently. 'What about shoes?'

'I bought some,' Tallitha said, revealing high-heeled, bronze, perfectly elegant sandals.

'Oh, just right!' Diana crowed. 'I know you'll be the belle of the ball.'

'I have no desire to be the belle of the ball,' Tallitha said wryly.

In fact, as the great day arrived, she found herself looking forward to it with some dread. And when Miles Gilmour said to her after lunch, 'Coming tonight, Tally-ho?' she replied, 'I'm not dying, so I must be.'

He cast her a laughing look. 'What's that supposed to mean?'

'Nothing,' she said hastily.

'Then why don't you take the afternoon off.'

'Oh. Oh no, I don't need to. Thank you all the same.'

'All the same you will, Miss Jones,' he said. 'You deserve it and I'm ordering you to, anyway!'

'But . . .'

'Tallitha.'

'Mr Gilmour?' she replied innocently. Then, 'But I'm quite organised, really I am!'

'I never knew a woman who was quite organised when it came to getting ready for a formal affair,' he said with a touch of mockery. 'Now are you going or do I have to take you home personally?'

'I . . . I'm going.'

Diana was delighted to see her home early because, unbeknown to Tallitha, she had plans to give her a facial and a manicure as well as doing her hair for her.

'Now we'll really be able to do it all properly,' she said with a glowing grin and Tallitha's heart contracted because Diana was, she knew, not only genuinely excited for her about this party, but enjoying the reflected excitement herself. If only she could go in my place, Tallitha thought. For that matter, if only she could meet some nice man who would love her for all her warmth and generosity. She just doesn't deserve to be living this half-life . . .

They sat Amanda on her bunny rug in the middle of the floor and set to work. And when she suddenly toppled backwards with a charmingly apologetic smile on to the pillow set behind her for just that purpose, Tallitha picked her up and nursed her, saying through stiff lips as Diana worked on her hair, 'I hope I don't frighten the life out of her with this stuff on my face.'

'Just don't laugh, you'll crack it!' Diana warned.

'I hope you don't mean my face.'

'You look just super,' Diana said as the taxi tooted

outside. She adjusted the velvet ribbon Tallitha wore around her neck—not with a cameo but a tiny antique gold-and-topaz butterfly that had belonged to Tallitha's mother pinned to it—and patted her hair, loose tonight in drifts of gleaming curls.

Tallitha moistened her lips, painted a soft apricot pink to match her nails. 'Are you sure? I feel perhaps we've overdone it.'

'No, we haven't,' Diana murmured and added poetically, 'You look young and with just a hint of a bygone age which adds a touch of mystery, but chic at the same time . . . you look lovely. Now, promise me you'll enjoy yourself?'

'I will. Thanks.' And she kissed Diana warmly.

For months afterwards, the old hands at Rathdowney, MacPherson & Gilmour maintained that it was a truly memorable Christmas party. And for weeks afterwards, at those gossipy lunchtime sessions in the canteen, the same theories were bandied about.

Had Miles Gilmour known? Or had the Rathdowneys sneaked it up on him? And wasn't she lovely even though she was pregnant? Lovely and, so it seemed, determined to heal the rift—well, keep it at bay for the night anyway. Why was she invited? Because she was a MacPherson, of course! A sleeping partner maybe, but all the same she had inherited a sizeable shareholding in the company from her father, hadn't she? Anyway, she always came to the Christmas party, although, yes, it did seem odd to invite Hayden Wentworth to a party Miles Gilmour was attending, but then again . . . And did you see them shake hands?

Tallitha saw it all.

She decided there was an air of unreality about it, about the whole night for that matter. Something to do, perhaps, with the fact that the canteen had been transformed from a not unpleasant but functional room to a Christmas wonderland; something to do with the colours of so many pretty dresses and formal suits—the sights of Miss Fortescue looking magnificent in midnight blue tulle but still with a fresh pink rosebud pinned to her dress; something to do with creating a minor sensation herself. 'Why, Tally! You look stunning—where did you get that dress?' Something to do with the elegantly set, white-clad tables; something to do with Sonia's boyfriend who had unfortunately big ears but one of the nicest smiles Tallitha had ever seen . . .

She saw Miles Gilmour looking darkly handsome in a dinner suit, which was apparently the expected dress for board members.

And she saw Heather Wentworth arrive wearing a blue spangled dress, that gave only the slightest indication of her condition and eclipsed every other dress at the party, and with that lovely haunting smile. She was greeted by Hugo Rathdowney and his tall, stern-looking wife with affection. And Leicester Rathdowney made a big fuss of her and boldly kissed her on the lips with a quizzical eyebrow raised at Hayden Wentworth, who was neither particularly young nor good-looking, but rather impressive somehow. In fact the look he cast Les Rathdowney was so openly derisive that a smile trembled on Tallitha's lips for a moment.

I do believe Hayden Wentworth and I have something in common, she thought, and then shivered suddenly for no reason at all that she could think of.

But what the electrified gathering was really waiting for, of course, turned out to be a damp squib. Heather Wentworth moved on to Miles Gilmour with that smile pinned firmly into place, and for a moment they stared at each other. Then his eyes softened and he said something to her which made that lovely, heart-breaking smile real somehow, then he shook hands with Hayden and they stood chatting quite normally for a few minutes.

'Oh, I'm so proud of him!' Sonia breathed in Tallitha's ear. 'I wasn't sure if they'd told him she was coming. Did they?'

'I don't know,' Tallitha whispered back. But I'm proud of him, too, she thought.

Contrary to her expectations Tallitha was quite in demand, not only by those who asked her to dance after the formalities of dinner were over, but by many people who stopped at Sonia's table to chat. And gradually the evening turned out to be less of an ordeal for her. But the highlight of it came early.

Miles Gilmour only danced with four people—thereby thwarting the heart's desire of quite a few girls—and his order of preference was typically his own. He danced the first dance of the night with Sonia, causing Mrs Rathdowney to look down her aristocratic nose with incredulity as Hayden Wentworth partnered her for this almost ceremonial first dance, and Hugo danced with Heather. But the radiant delight it brought to Sonia outshone every raised eyebrow, and Tallitha knew that Sonia would treasure this honour for the rest of her life. Then he asked Tallitha to dance the next dance with him.

She said, as he swung her into his arms, 'That was the nicest thing to do!'

He looked briefly surprised. 'I like Sonia.'

'I know,' Tallitha said softly. 'She's the only person you never get cross with.'

'I . . . That would be unfair.' He shrugged.

'I know. Not everyone's so . . . fair, though,' she said.

'But it's not her fault.'

'No.'

They danced in silence for a while. Then he held her away from him and said with a comprehensive glance from the top of her curls to the tips of her sandals, 'You're looking very lovely tonight, Tallitha. Another new dress?'

'Mmm. Very new.'

'You look—You remind me of . . .' He stopped dancing and studied her critically: her slender neck with the brown ribbon and the gold butterfly, her smooth, pale shoulders, her small oval face looking up at him expectantly. 'I don't know,' he confessed with a grimace. 'A mystery lady, it seems. Are you enjoying yourself?' he asked, moving to the music again and with just a hint of a frown in his eyes, as if he was really puzzled.

'Oh yes. Are . . .' She bit her lip.

'Am I?'

'Well . . . yes.'

'I'm enjoying dancing with you,' he said. 'You're really very good at it, you know.'

'I believe I got carted to every country dance around for miles even before I could walk. My mother loved it. It was the one pleasure she allowed herself.'

'Even after your father died?'

'Yes. But country dances are like that. Everyone goes, from babies in their baskets to grandmothers.'

'So you're an old hand at this kind of thing?'

'I wouldn't say that,' she answered with a wry smile.

The other two ladies Miles Gilmour honoured by dancing with them were Miss Fortescue and Mrs

Rathdowney—the latter of whom gave the distinct impression she didn't really approve of him until about half-way through their dance, when she relented and was even heard to laugh at something he said.

'Mr Gilmour could charm a stone,' Miss Fortescue, who had stopped at Sonia's table to sit and chat for a while, remarked as she observed this.

'I've noticed that,' Tallitha agreed a little ruefully.

Miss Fortescue turned to her. 'I gather you've somewhat changed your opinion of him, Miss Jones,' she said with an uncharacteristic twinkle in her eye.

'On his better days—no, you're right, I have changed my opinion of him,' Tallitha said.

'Well, I think this is a good opportunity for me to congratulate you, Tallitha—may I call you that? You've done very well and I know he's very pleased with you. In fact he told me the other day he was petrified a vacancy in Travel would come up and he'd lose you.'

'Did he really say that?'

'He certainly did!'

Tallitha felt as if she was grinning all over her face.

'Hasn't he mentioned it to you?' Miss Fortescue asked curiously.

'Yes, but—he teases me quite a lot.'

After that the evening was made, Tallitha felt, and no doubt it was responsible for the mood of vivaciousness she found herself in and the odd thought that struck her: I really didn't want to come to this party but here I am *really* enjoying myself!

But at midnight, although the revelry showed no sign of abating, her spirits flagged suddenly—all because the Wentworths left.

Tallitha noticed how it happened quite by accident.

She *had* cautioned herself not to spend the evening staring curiously, even though she couldn't help being curious. But she was alone at the table for once, gratefully sipping a cool drink, when the Wentworths stopped dancing right in front of her and Hayden said to his wife, 'You look tired.'

Tallitha saw Heather sigh and heard her say, 'I am. Could we—could we go now?'

But what all but took Tallitha's breath away was the sudden blaze of concern in Hayden Wentworth's eyes as he said, 'Why didn't you tell me? Come . . .' And he led her away.

He loves her—he really loves her too, Tallitha thought with wide eyes and parted lips. That's why he won't let her go—it's as simple as that. No, it still doesn't make sense, because that's nothing tangible to hold someone with. Perhaps she loves them both? Can that happen? And perhaps she's torn between the two of them?

Five minutes later the Wentworths had left with the minimum of ceremony and Miles Gilmour was staring at the door, his eyes dark and his mouth hard. Then he turned away deliberately and picked up his drink.

And that was when Tallitha decided to leave herself. Sonia tried to talk her out of it, saying, 'Oh, things are only just hotting up, Tally!'

But she slipped away all the same, intending to ring for a taxi at the public phone in the canteen lobby which was dim and quiet, the sound of the band muffled behind the heavy swing doors.

Ten minutes, the taxi company said, so she waited for about five of them in the lobby, then started down the corridor towards the lift.

Unfortunately, Les Rathdowney chose that time to leave the party too, and he came up behind her silently and tapped her on the shoulder, nearly causing her to die of fright.

'Well, well,' he drawled, 'if it isn't Miss Jones! Party too tame for you, too?'

He slurred his words just slightly and a shiver of apprehension ran down her spine but she said firmly, 'No. I'm just tired, that's all.'

'Well, you could put it like that,' he drawled. 'Tired of being on one's best behaviour—it's the same thing. Now, why don't we go on somewhere else? I know a few lively places, Miss Jones, where my papa and mama wouldn't be breathing down our necks; nor, for that matter, would Miles Gilmour be,' he said significantly and stared at her boldly.

The lift came as Tallitha said, 'No thank you,' and she hesitated before stepping into it. He followed her and the doors slid closed.

'You know, he can't dictate to you after office hours, Tallitha—such a pretty name, by the way,' he murmured, his brown eyes roaming up and down her body. 'And there'll come a day when he won't be able to dictate to me at any time.' He steadied himself with a hand on the wall as the lift started to move downwards.

Tallitha said nothing, just stared at the floor.

Les Rathdowney chuckled then. 'My, my, what a loyal little secretary you are,' he marvelled, as the lift reached the ground floor and they stepped out together into the silent, deserted main lobby. He put out a hand and closed his fingers about her wrist. 'You know I've wondered about that. Occurred to me that Miles might have warned me off for reasons other than my wasting his precious time. Occurred to me, to be frank about it, Miss Jones, that he might be having you on the side. But you know, there's no future in that for you, not with Miles. But . . .'

Tallitha's free hand flashed up and caught Les Rathdowney a stinging blow square on his cheek. 'You ... bastard,' she whispered. 'You low-down little creep!'

But after a grunt of surprise he started to laugh. 'So Dad was right!' he said delightedly, but his tone changed abruptly as Tallitha went to hit him again and he swore viciously and hauled her into his arms and lowered his head to kiss her brutally.

'*No!*' she breathed, trying to twist her mouth away.

'Why not? If Miles can get it so can I. Keep still, for God's sake!'

But Tallitha began to fight in earnest then, with her fists, her nails, the heels of her shoes. And possibly because he was drunk, the ferocity of her attack took him by surprise and he staggered and tripped over backwards to sit heavily on the marble floor.

But she wasn't finished, it seemed. She lifted her evening bag to aim a solid blow at his head. It was not a particularly substantial bag, but the intention was undoubtedly there—when someone said in a hard, authoritative voice, '*Tallitha!*'

CHAPTER FIVE

IT was Miles Gilmour.

The lift doors closed behind him, and Tallitha lowered her arm and started to shake uncontrollably. Miles came right up to her, took one look at her swollen lips and disordered hair, and turned to Les Rathdowney. 'I ought to flatten you, Les,' he said through his teeth. 'Maybe I will later. Get going!'

Les opened his mouth but thought better of it. He stood up unsteadily, glared incredulously at Tallitha, then turned away to stumble down the stairs that led to the basement car park.

'It's all right,' Miles said turning back to Tallitha and putting an arm around her. But she flinched and shuddered and pulled away.

'Tallitha,' he said grimly, 'it's *me*.'

She stared up at him and then tears obscured her vision and she relaxed against him whispering, 'I'm sorry . . . oh, God!' And she wept helplessly into his shoulder.

'Taxi!' a strange voice called impatiently through the foyer doors.

'Th-that's mine,' Tallitha stammered and tried to free herself again.

But he wouldn't let her go. Instead he pulled some money from his pocket and handed it to the taxi driver who had come inside. 'There's been a mix-up,' he said. 'Sorry.'

The taxi driver looked at the note and saluted him. 'Happens all the time,' he said happily.

'But ... but I've got to get home somehow,' Tallitha objected.

'I'll fix that. In fact I've thought of a better idea,' Miles Gilmour said sombrely with one arm still around her, supporting her. 'And please don't argue.'

He took her to his apartment—a penthouse that overlooked the Brisbane River, upstream to the city, and the Victoria and William Jolly Bridges, the new Cultural Centre and Art Gallery and the Queen Elizabeth fountain.

Tallitha hesitated in the car park and looked at him with huge, darkened eyes.

He said evenly, 'I think you must be aware by now that I have no intentions of seducing you or harming you in any way.'

'. . . Yes,' she whispered.

'I think the time's also come to talk to *someone* about this deep dark secret of yours, and I know there is one, Tallitha, just as I know you can't go on for ever bottling it up. Apart from anything else, it's dangerous. Do you see that?' His dark blue gaze was suddenly piercing.

She closed her eyes. 'Yes . . .'

'All right then.'

Now she was standing on his terrace amidst the potted palm trees, gazing with stunned eyes at the beauty of the view—the lights reflected in the river, the sparse, pure, elegant lines of the floodlit Victoria Bridge, the high white moon above Brisbane city.

A sound came behind her and she turned to see Miles with two mugs of coffee. 'Sit down,' he said. 'It's nice out here, isn't it?'

'It's marvellous. I . . .' She sat down and clenched her hands in her lap, not knowing where to begin and with a cold hand of fear clutching at her heart anyway. Why did I agree to this? she thought in sudden panic.

'Tallitha?' he said quietly but imperatively.

She drew a deep breath. Just try to make it factual, she warned herself. 'I think it all started way back,' she said shakily. 'At least that's an excuse I often make to myself. But I did sometimes feel on the outer as a kid—the housekeeper's daughter. Of course some families weren't like that but some were, although it didn't really bother me until I was about fifteen. Then I began to feel a bit like Cinderella.' She grimaced and sipped her coffee and spluttered slightly.

'It's spiked,' he said.

'Oh. Well, by the time I was seventeen we had moved to a new station, a big one. But we'd only been there about six months when my mother died.' She was silent for a moment then she went on, 'They got another housekeeper, but I'd finished with school and they kept me on to look after the two youngest children of the family. I quite enjoyed it because they weren't that young and it was a change from nappies. The eldest of the family was . . .'

Her voice cracked and she looked up at the moon. 'Was like a Greek god to me,' she said barely audibly. 'Fair, very good-looking, a few years older and back from a very expensive schooling and a couple of years at the Gatton Agricultural College . . . I fell hopelessly, silently in love.'

'It happens,' Miles Gilmour commented.

'Yes. Only I made one cardinal mistake,' she murmured after a while, looking down at her cup again. 'I assumed, when he started to take an interest in me, that the same thing had happened for him.'

'It hadn't?'

'No. I should have known when he was so secretive

about it. But I never really stopped to think, to wonder why, to—wonder whether we were really kindred spirits. I was just dizzy with delight, I guess. Cinderella had come into her own. How insanely stupid can you be?' she said bitterly.

'It's a notorious age for it, Tallitha.'

She stared down at her coffee cup. 'It might be. All the same, I couldn't . . . still can't, believe how I could have let myself down like that, not to mention my mother.'

'What happened?'

'The usual,' she said after a time, staring straight ahead now. 'He persuaded me to let him make love to me. He made it sound as if it was the mature, adult thing to do and certainly what he expected of his girlfriend—oh, the usual pressures silly little girls succumb to because no one can really make them understand how it can ruin their lives. Eventually I gave in. It . . . I . . . It was horrible. I was petrified of falling pregnant, although he said he knew what he was doing. But I don't think he knew much about it at all, really. Or perhaps he never will. Because he changed—there was no tenderness about it, only an awful furtiveness and haste. He couldn't wait to get my clothes off, he tore them and then . . . and then he was so heavy, and I couldn't believe anything could hurt so much.' She closed her eyes.

Miles leant across and put a hand on her arm. 'I'm sorry. I thought it might have been something like that.'

She smiled painfully. 'It happened again and if anything it was worse, although he said it would be much better. But after that second time I was beginning to come to my senses. He not only hurt me but he frightened me. It was as if I was just a body, and he didn't seem to care if I was hurt or frightened. Then when I said no to him, he ... sort of attacked me and called me all the unpleasant names under the sun—and he dropped me like a hot brick. Perhaps he would have anyway. Unfortunately, I came to my senses too late, because I was pregnant.' She lifted her lashes and looked starkly across at Miles Gilmour. 'You knew—somehow you guessed something like that, didn't you? I've often wondered how.'

'An educated guess,' he said. 'A lot of the agony that comes to a young woman revolves around that kind of thing. What happened to the baby?'

'I lost it. I miscarried at three months. It might have been the best thing that could have happened, and before it did, in my heart of hearts, I thought that it would be. But when it did I felt different, as if I'd lost a part of myself, as if ... I don't know, but I wished it hadn't.'

'What caused it?'

'Nothing. It was just one of those pregnancies destined to terminate, the doctor told me. In fact he told me there was no reason why I shouldn't sail through the next one.' She winced.

'And where were you? Still on the station?'

'I ... got packed off in disgrace.'

'Tell me,' he said gently.

'Well, I put off and put off admitting to myself that I was pregnant. I used to get up every day and say to myself, I'll find out today that I'm not. But I went on deluding myself for so long that the new housekeeper, who was a nice person, guessed and made me tell her everything. It was my eighteenth birthday that day. I shouldn't have done that, told her I mean, because she ... Well, it wasn't pleasant for her either, and she really needed that job. But I was just feeling so sick and scared. Anyway, she went to the boss and his wife and told them.'

'Let me guess,' Miles Gilmour said. 'They didn't believe it of their son?'

'They consulted him, then they came back and accused me of having seduced him, probably with the aim of forcing him to marry me. So they felt entitled to wash their hands of the whole affair, they said. Although they gave me some money to . . . to have an abortion. I didn't want to take it. I couldn't. I hated the thought of that somehow, and I knew my mother would have turned over in her grave, if she hadn't already.'

'Go on,' he said after a time during which Tallitha wiped away some tears.

'Mrs Bell, the housekeeper, told me I would be mad not to, even if I didn't use it for that. She really tried to help. She even found out where I could go for counselling and so on, down to Toowoomba, and I was going to go, but . . .'

'You miscarried. It would have been a miracle if you hadn't suffered some trauma,' he said drily. 'So what happened them?'

'I drifted around getting jobs in country pubs and so on, trying to save as much as I could to give me some sort of security, because my mother hadn't ever been able to save much. There's not much else to do out there anyway, but it was no good,' she said bitterly.

'Not for a basically naïve eighteen-year-old it wouldn't have been.'

'It wasn't only that. It was bad enough fighting off complete strangers, but one day I found out that I'd acquired a reputation. That Brad . . .' She bit her lip and took a couple of deep breaths but couldn't go on.

'That Brad had spread the word?' he said after a time.

She dropped her face into her hands. '*Yes,*' she wept. 'I suppose having red hair and a name like Tallitha didn't help, not out there where the bush telegraph works like wildfire. And I knew the word was just going to keep on spreading. That's when I decided to come to Brisbane although I still didn't have very much money—abortions can't be very dear,' she said with a twisted smile. 'But I thought *nothing* could be worse than that . . . th-that awful, naked feeling. Oh God . . .'

Miles Gilmour stood up and lifted her to her feet and held her in his arms. 'You poor kid,' he said, and stroked her hair gently while a great tide of weeping racked her body. 'Listen to me,' he said eventually. 'There's no name bad enough to call him; it's as simple as that, my dear.'

'But I should have been able to work that out before!'

'You're being too hard on yourself, Tallitha, believe me,' he said softly and held her closer.

It was a long time before she was finally still, just resting against him with that awful tide of hysteria receding. Then she said shakily, 'Thanks. I'm sorry.'

'No need to be,' he murmured and released her. 'Come inside. I think it's going to rain.'

She looked upwards to see that a bank of heavy cloud, silver at the edges, was obscuring the moon.

'Feeling better now?' he asked. He had poured her a stiff looking drink and she was sipping it gratefully.

'Yes I am, really,' she said and smiled wanly. 'You'd think I'd have got over it by now, wouldn't you? Actually, I have. I mean I don't go around dwelling on it. It's just . . . that it catches me unawares sometimes, although tonight was a bit different somehow.' She frowned abstractedly. 'I wasn't so much frightened as angry and *disgusted*. But what I'm trying to say is that I don't go round feeling sorry for myself.'

Miles Gilmour regarded her thoughtfully from across the room. He'd poured himself a drink, too, and taken off his dinner jacket and was lying back in a jade green velvet-covered armchair. The room was beautifully decorated in shades of green and gold and pink with some exquisite antique vases and lamps, and paintings.

'Perhaps you should,' he said eventually.

She stared at him.

'I mean, perhaps you should stop blaming yourself so much. It happened. It happens all the time and in your case the consequences were pretty dreadful. But that doesn't make *you* any worse than thousands of vulnerable young girls who escape that particular pitfall. The other thing is, if you've in no way encouraged Les, and I know you haven't, he was totally at fault tonight, not you. Or do you think you're branded with an invisible sign of some kind that allows men to think you're fair game because of what happened to you?'

Tallitha licked her lips. 'I've never really thought of it like that, I mean in those words, but you could be right.' She paused then said slowly. 'It . . . it could be something like that.'

'That's ridiculous,' he said, but gently.

'I know,' she agreed helplessly, and added with an effort, 'But about Les. You were shocked at the way I reacted, weren't you? But you . . .'

'Advised you to scratch his eyes out once?' he said ironically. 'I know, and I regret it now, Tallitha. It wasn't the best advice. Not all men are gentlemen, and it could be dangerous. I'm afraid Les could be a bad enemy.'

'Gentlemen like you?' she said after a while.

He smiled slightly and shrugged. 'I don't get my kicks out of overpowering little girls. Actually, you were probably right in the first place about the best way to handle him.'

A glimmer of a smile lit Tallitha's eyes, then they clouded and grew confused again. 'I was just so angry,' she said.

He was silent for a time, then he said with a rueful little smile, 'Since I'm playing amateur psychologist, you know what I think is the real problem now? The fact that you're isolating yourself so much. For one thing, you're making it nearly impossible for you to meet someone who can prove to you that not *all* men are like that—you don't honestly believe that, do you?'

'Sometimes it's hard not to,' she said, thinking of Diana. 'But no, I suppose not. It's just become a habit now, I guess. Do you know, the last firm on earth I wanted to work for was Rathdowney, MacPherson & Gilmour, with its outback connections. And if I hadn't been looking down a tunnel of years on the dole, I'd never have taken it when the C.E.S. came up with it. I spent the first six months or so petrified I was going to run into someone who knew Brad, if not he himself or his family. It becomes a habit to wonder who *knows*, and to want to crawl into a hole and hide. It's not easy.'

'Of course not, but it's never going to become any easier this way. You *need* people. Because once you see the value they place on you and not your past, that they don't care what happened to you once, then you can start to value yourself.'

'It's funny you should say that,' Tallitha murmured, 'but tonight ...' She stopped abruptly as things fell into place in her mind with a suddenness that jolted her. It hadn't been so much the memories tonight, after all, had it?'

'Go on,' Miles said.

'Oh, it doesn't matter.'

'Tallitha, tell me. Something to do with Les?' he hazarded.

She bit her lip.

'I can always ask him,' Miles insisted on a suddenly steely note.

'You're the *last* person he'd ... I mean ...'

'Oh, I see,' he said after a pause, during which he'd searched her hot, embarrassed face penetratingly. 'He implied you were somewhat more than my secretary?' he said flatly.

She looked away and then back at him. 'Yes.'

'And that made you angry?'

'*Yes*. Mixed in with everything else, it did. Not only because it's not true and never could be true, but because it seemed to strike at what you said just now. I ... Being your secretary has meant a great deal to me in terms of, well, as you said, value. And I hated him for dragging it all through the mud like that, and for trying to denigrate you like that when you've been so terrific to me,' she said huskily.

Miles Gilmour studied her for a moment in silence and she couldn't read his expression at all. Then he said, 'And I, my dear, don't think anyone has said anything as nice to me for years. Nor defended my honour so stoutly, perhaps ever. Which is a little incongruous,' he added.

'Not to me, it isn't,' she whispered.

He laughed and stood up to come over to her. 'I'm

tempted to tell you not to change a hair of your head or anything about you,' he said, drawing her to her feet and smiling down at her in a way that made her heart beat suddenly faster, as it so often did these days, 'but that would be supremely selfish. Look, I'm going to take you home now but I want you to promise me one thing first.' His eyes sobered. 'Put it all behind you now, Tallitha, and start to believe in yourself and trust yourself enough to start living again. Will you?'

She closed her eyes. 'Yes.'

He dropped a light kiss on her hair.

Tallitha stared at herself in her own bathroom mirror and saw shadows beneath her eyes, and a complete lack of make-up, but then it would have been a miracle if any of it had survived the trauma of the night. She saw a query in her green eyes, the nature of which made her heart beat faster and her mouth feel dry and her hands tremble.

Wouldn't it be supremely ironic, she thought, if Miles Gilmour himself were to be the one person—man, rather—to touch my heart when I thought it had been frozen, in that way, for ever?

'Oh no,' she whispered. 'Don't let *that* happen to me. Please, not Miles, not the *last* one I could ever have . . .

'Tallitha, do you realise you're overdue for your holiday?'

Tallitha looked up from her typewriter, startled. 'Well, yes, Mr Gilmour—Actually, no. I'd forgotten about it,' she conceded wryly.

Miles Gilmour strolled over to sit on the corner of her desk. It was two weeks since the Christmas party and a week to go until Christmas. It was also a period during which Tallitha had convinced herself that her fears were groundless. Of course she liked him very much, admired him, and, anyway, wasn't it a well-known fact that doctors and confidants became the objects of much admiration from their patients?

But that she'd fallen in love with him, was out of the question. She'd gone out of her way to be as businesslike as possible since that night, so he wouldn't have cause to regret becoming involved in her sordid past—strike that word, she'd mused, and substitute plain past.

'I was talking to Miss Fortescue when the subject came up. She suggested you and I work out a mutually suitable time. From my point of view there's no such thing, but, as Miss Fortescue pointed out, I shall have to be brave about it.'

Tallitha's green gaze was amused. 'I'm sure she said no such thing,' she murmured.

'Oh yes she did. When she gets me on my own, she treats me like a schoolboy—possibly because she's known me since those days. She used to work for my father and after my mother died, if it hadn't been for her, neither my sister nor I would ever have got to the dentist, had our birthdays remembered—Dad was supremely absent-minded about things like that—or a host of other things. We used to call her Frosty and tell her all our troubles. Incidentally, she also offered me a little girl from the typing pool to replace you. You'll have to show her the ropes.'

'Oh! Well, whatever you like—I really don't mind waiting until . . .'

'No, we might as well get it out of the way. Anyway,' he looked at her critically, 'you're looking a bit pale. I've probably been overworking you, unless you're still dwelling on that night?'

'Oh no,' she said hastily. 'And I haven't even seen Mr Rathdowney since then.'

'That's because he hasn't been here,' Miles Gilmour said a shade grimly. 'I thought a tour of the backblocks might remind him of whence he came and ... cool his ardour somewhat. He's doing a short statistical survey for me.'

Tallitha stared at her boss.

'He *is* under my jurisdiction at the moment,' he murmured. 'But to get back to your holiday, straight after Christmas is probably the best time for me. New Year and most of January are traditionally slack times, times when it's hard to get anything done because so many people are on holiday. But it doesn't give you much time to get organised.'

'That's no problem,' she said tranquilly. 'I hadn't planned to go away except down to the Gold Coast for a few days, perhaps, and that's easy enough to organise at short notice.'

'Don't you think it would be a good idea to take a proper holiday?' he queried abruptly. 'The kind where you'd meet people?'

She looked away and coloured faintly. 'I was planning that and saving for it, for my next one after this,' she said quietly. 'And I *am* meeting people. I've joined a tennis club—we both have, Diana and I. We had our first game on Sunday.'

'Bravo,' he said softly. 'How was it?'

'It was good,' she confessed. 'They seemed to be a really nice crowd of people. And afterwards we had a barbecue—a Christmas party really—and everyone took their kids so that was no problem for Diana. It was really great how they welcomed us, seeing it was our first day.'

'Well, I'm glad at least one Christmas party turned out well for you. What are you doing over Christmas?

It's a four-day break including the weekend.'

'Well, as it's Amanda's first Christmas,' she said with a smile, 'we're going to have a joint tree with all the trimmings and presents and a turkey and so on. Boxing Day we're going to Lone Pine Sanctuary to introduce her to the koalas and the kangaroos and have a picnic—hold thumbs it doesn't rain!' she said wryly.

'My God!' he marvelled. 'That brings back memories! From the time I was six that was a special treat once a year, to go up the river to Lone Pine and have a picnic. Well, it seems as if Christmas is taken care of nicely.'

'Yes. What are you doing?'

He grimaced. 'Spending the day with my sister and her tribe, being a dutiful uncle no doubt and helping to break in all the new cricket bats and erect all the new tents.'

'How many nephews have you got?' she asked with a laugh.

'Four. And one niece. Actually I was thinking of asking your advice about what to get a girl of ten for Christmas.'

'That depends on the girl. I suppose with four brothers she's quite a tomboy?'

'No, she's not, she's essentially feminine and she rules them with a rod of iron.'

'A dress, then? Tallitha suggested. 'A really special dress. From what I remember of being ten, a frilly dress was my number one priority.'

'Did you get one?'

'Yes, I did. My mother made it.'

'You wouldn't . . .' He paused and cocked an eyebrow at her.

'Not at all,' she said with a grin, 'if you give me some details. You don't mean make it?'

'No, buy it, naturally.'

'I'd like to. Anyway, what are private secretaries for?'

'Then you wouldn't like to help me out with my sister at the same time? She's also very feminine despite being *the* ultimate authority in the family on most things.'

'She must be a lot like you,' Tallitha said innocently. 'Well, all right. So long as you don't want me to . . .' She bit her lip.

'What?'

'Nothing,' she said hastily.

'My dear Tallitha,' he drawled, eyeing her wickedly, 'you know you never get away with that with me. I'm just as liable to sit here and drive you mad until you tell me!'

'Oh no, you're not!' she replied tartly. 'You've got an appointment in ten minutes, for one thing.'

'That gives me *plenty* of time to wrest it from you. Come on, spill the beans,' he said imperiously.

'Oh! You're . . .'

'Don't say it,' he warned.

'Well, you are. I was only going to say as long as you don't expect me to buy a Christmas present for your . . . Well, you haven't got a wife, but you know what I mean,' she said crossly.

'Ah.' His lips quivered. 'I swear it never crossed my mind! You don't approve of that, by the sound of it?'

'No I don't,' she retorted.

'Getting one's secretary to do it or not having a wife but the other kind of lady to buy presents for?'

Tallitha took a deep breath. 'Mr Gilmour . . .'

'Miss Jones?'

They stared at each other, she exasperatedly, he quite seriously.

'Oh, will you go and do some work!' she said finally. 'And let *me* get on with mine—of which, in case you've forgotten, there's a mountain!'

'. . . Er, Miss Jones?' a strange voice said from the passage doorway, and they both looked round to see a startled, deeply embarrassed-looking girl standing there.

'I'm sorry, I did knock,' she said timidly, 'but I don't think you heard me. Miss Fortescue sent me up to . . . to . . .'

'Of course!' Miles Gilmour stood up. 'You're Miss Laidley from the typing pool, aren't you? And you've come up to be taught how to take over when Miss Jones goes on holiday. She's an excellent teacher, I can vouch for that,' he said confidentially. 'Particularly in secretary stroke boss relations—how to deal with the monster, in other words. I'm going back to work, Miss Jones,' he added. 'Like a lamb.' He closed the inner door very gently behind him.

Miss Laidley turned nervous, confused eyes upon Tallitha, who closed her own eyes briefly and ground her teeth.

'I thought he had a terrible temper,' the other girl said. 'But it sounded as if *you* were telling *him* off.'

'I wasn't . . . I was . . . He does.' Tallitha broke off and stared at Janet Laidley, who she knew slightly, and found herself wondering if Miss Fortescue had suddenly gone mad. For Janet was little more than a child, hopelessly shy and the very last person to inflict Miles Gilmour upon, whether he was losing his temper or driving one mad the other way.

She tried again. 'Oh, he can be a bit difficult sometimes but . . . Well, he can also be very nice. The thing is not to let him frighten you.'

'He's already done that,' Janet Laidley confessed.

'He used to frighten me until I got to know him better. You'll see,' Tallitha said firmly. 'Now, where shall we start?' But she was thinking, I don't somehow *think* this is going to work . . .

Two days before Christmas, she had somewhat changed her mind and she brought the matter up with her boss, but only after she had shown him the Christmas presents.

'In the end I made the dress,' she said a little diffidently. 'I couldn't find one nice enough but I spent the money on this beautiful musical box—it's also a jewel box. See how the china figurines dance when the music plays?'

'Yes,' he said slowly and picked up the dress, a delicious concoction of yellow dotted voile with an attached half-slip trimmed with lace. 'Well, now,' he said, 'I'm not an expert but this looks as if it could have come from the finest boutique. You're a genius, Tallitha!'

'No I'm not,' she laughed. 'But I can sew and I had this vision of a dress, but I just couldn't find one like it. I got some long lace socks to go with it. I hope she likes it . . . I'm sure she'll like the musical box.'

He didn't seem that interested in the musical box, in fact he was still staring at the dress now laid on the desk.

'And for your sister I got . . .'

'Tally, I must owe you some more money,' he said abruptly. 'You must have spent hours on this, it's a work of art.'

She coloured. 'Oh no. I enjoyed it.'

'But . . .'

'No, please, Mr Gilmour,' she said very quietly. 'You'll make me sorry I did it.'

He regarded her silently for a moment. 'All right,' he said at length with a slight smile. 'I'll just say thank you very much, sweet Tally-ho!'

She said hastily, 'And for your sister, I got this perfectly elegant Italian leather bag.' She produced the slim clutch bag of soft aqua calf with distinctive bands of amethyst snakeskin around it. 'It has a matching purse and key case, see?' It had also cost a small fortune, she remembered but did not say. In fact, the amount of money she'd been given to spend on Miles Gilmour's sister and niece had quite taken her breath away and for his sister, anyway, she'd at first been totally unable to imagine what she could spend it on. Until she'd started to look around the more exclusive gift shops, then she'd had the opposite problem.

'Think she'll like it?'

'It looks very much like Susan's kind of thing.'

'Oh good. Would you like me to wrap them? I got some really nice paper and stuff.'

'Heaven knows what I did before you came, Miss Jones!'

'*I* know,' she replied.

'Well, yes,' he agreed, not in the least shamefaced, 'but none of my other secretaries has shown such taste.'

'I'm honoured by that compliment, Mr Gilmour,' she said demurely, picking up the dress.

'You're also laughing at me, Miss Jones,' he retorted.

'Not at all. Oh, talking of secretaries, there's something I wanted to bring to your attention.'

'Miss Laidley?' he hazarded, and lay back in his chair. 'Has she died of fright yet?'

'No, she has not. Which is not to say it can't

happen,' she murmured and he winced, but laughingly. 'But she's very bright, you know,' she went on determinedly. 'Actually, she's quite surprised me. She really thinks before she does anything, she remembers what she's been told and she's a fast and accurate typist. So . . .' She paused and glanced at Miles Gilmour to see that he was looking at her with a world of lazy amusement in his dark blue eyes.

'I promise I won't,' he said. 'I'll treat her with kid gloves.'

Tallitha bit her lip.

'That was what you were going to request of me, wasn't it?' he drawled.

'That, and that you don't, well, tease her too much. She's a bit shy, you see, and it could be as difficult for her to handle as the other thing.'

He sat up. 'My dear Tallitha, I've just had a brainwave. Why don't you go out and buy me a muzzle? That way I won't be able to say or do much to the poor girl at all!' he said indignantly.

But Tallitha was in the process of fleeing his office.

Christmas Eve dawned bright and hot.

Tallitha found on her desk, when she arrived at work, an envelope bearing a bonus cheque, the amount of which made her blink. But when she tried to thank Miles Gilmour, he waved her away, saying it was company policy.

She spent the morning trying to tie up the last loose ends with Janet Laidley, a process which was somewhat erratic because of the number of people who called on Miles Gilmour to administer and receive Christmas cheer. He had laid in a number of bottles of champagne, but eventually the crowd got so large that they spilled into the outer office and Janet and Tallitha found themselves sipping champagne, too.

The company was closing officially for the Christmas break at two o'clock in the afternoon, but the party was still going strong. At three, Miles looked at his watch and said to Tallitha and Janet, 'Hell, you're supposed to be gone, you two!'

'Someone will need to clear up, though,' Tallitha murmured.

'I'll stay and do that,' Janet offered, surprising them and herself apparently, because she blushed.

Tallitha opened her mouth, but she received such a speaking, laughing look from her boss, which said quite clearly, I'll look after her and see that no one gets fresh with her, etc., that a wry little smile twisted her lips. 'All right. Well, happy Christmas, Mr Gilmour.' She put out her hand.

'And to you, too, Miss Jones.' He shook her hand. 'And have a nice holiday.' But there was something in his eyes that puzzled her. Something wicked ... 'Oh, and don't worry about us. We're going to get along like a house on fire, aren't we, Miss Laidley?'

'Well, I think we are,' Janet said with naïve surprise.

'I'm sure you will,' was all Tallitha could think of saying. Then, just as she was thinking that for some reason she devoutly mistrusted that look in his eye, some new arrivals claimed him, and she turned away and left quietly. Feeling ... Feeling how? she asked herself. Let down, flat. Because I won't be seeing him for three and a half weeks? Don't be a fool, Tallitha Jones, don't be a fool ...

But it was a foolish tear she was blinking away as

she walked out of Rathdowney House into the bright,
hot sunlight.

'Of course you must go! Diana, sit down and listen to
me . . .'

She'd got home to find Diana pacing her flat,
looking a picture of distress and indecision. The
reason for it had not been immediately clear because
she'd tried to pretend to Tallitha that nothing was
wrong. Then she'd burst into tears and the whole
story had come out. Her mother had sent a telegram
asking Diana to ring her, and on the phone made it
clear that she and Diana's father wanted to patch up
their differences with her, and desperately wanted
Diana and Amanda home for Christmas.

'It was never Mum really,' she wept. 'She must
have been working on Dad all these months. H-he
came on the phone, too, and asked me to forgive him.
He said he'd drive all the way in to pick me up this
evening. Oh, I don't know what to do!'

'But you said you'd go, didn't you?' Tallitha asked
urgently.

'Yes . . . yes . . . But I thought of you as soon as I
put the phone down. I can still get him, he won't have
left just yet . . .'

'Don't you dare! Honey, listen to me. This could
affect your whole life. With their love and their
support things are going to be so much easier for you,
and think of Amanda!'

'But what will you do? It's Christmas and we were
going to have it together.'

'Do you know, for this to happen is the best thing I
could wish for Christmas. Look, you've told me what
your father's like and I think this must be a big thing
for him to have done. So don't even think of putting

up obstacles! Just go and show him how much you love him and your mother. I promise you, Amanda will do the rest, you'll see.'

'I . . . Perhaps you could come, too?' Diana said with a ray of hope.

'No, love,' Tallitha said wisely, 'better for it to be just the four of you. Now are you going to pack or shall I do it for you?'

But as she waved Diana off later that night, and her stern patrician-looking father who had looked once at his granddaughter, then turned to take his daughter in his arms with tears in his eyes, Tallitha felt a bubble of emotion rise to her throat.

But it's only because I feel so happy for them, she told herself. And because it seems that Christmas still can produce some miracles . . .

CHAPTER SIX

THE turkey had been cooked because it had defrosted anyway, the wine opened, even the pudding warmed despite it being a blindingly hot day.

And the Christmas tree stood in the corner of Tallitha's bed-sitting room, dressed in its glittering gold and silver and red decorations which had so fascinated Amanda. Even Mason had a decoration on the top of his cage, but being Mason he found it not fascinating but quite irritating.

Tallitha stared at the remains of the meal and wondered why she had bothered. For there was far, far more of the Christmas lunch left than had been eaten. It will be cold roast turkey or casseroled turkey for the rest of the week, she mused and, with a sigh, started to clear up.

At two o'clock she turned on the television to watch *The Nutcracker* and for the next couple of hours lost herself in the ballet. But as the last lovely notes of the Waltz of the Flowers faded away, she found herself in the grip of a mood of haunting sadness. She moved restlessly in the chair she was curled up in as if to ward it off physically, but did not succeed. And it became more. Perhaps, she thought dimly, as she started to shake and cry, because I've been battening down on it for so long now. But *this* lonely day has defeated me . . .

It was a torrent of emotion that battered her physically and mentally. It was far worse than the tears she'd cried when baring her soul to Miles

Gilmour because even then she'd held back so much—that awful, frighteningly alone feeling she'd worked so desperately to hold at bay for years. But it was claiming her now, sweeping away every ounce of the self-reliance she'd built up so painstakingly, reducing her to a state of sheer, blind panic.

'Why?' she wept. 'Why now? I've spent Christmas alone before. Oh God, you were wrong, Miles. If I'd never expected anything more of today, I wouldn't have minded being alone. But I've made myself vulnerable again and never more so than with . . . you . . .'

And as she cried and couldn't stop—cried because she realised, and would never be able to deny it again, that a pivotal root of this crisis was the fact that she *had* committed the supreme irony, she had fallen desperately in love with Miles Gilmour—she didn't know that great storm clouds had built up, didn't hear the rain or know that it had cooled down. All she could think was that with Diana and Amanda present she might have been able to go on battening down, but that with no one she hadn't stood a chance.

It was Mason uttering a squawk that caused her to lift her head at last. And then she thought she was hallucinating, that she'd lost her mind as her tear-drenched eyes rested on the tall figure standing stock still in the open doorway to her private veranda. Miles . . .

Miles with three gaily wrapped presents in his hands. Miles saying, 'I came to play Father Christmas.' Miles putting the presents down carefully. All this like a dream, like the dream sequences of the ballet.

Then she saw his eyes change and heard him say on a note of concern and tenderness, 'What's happened? What's gone wrong?'

'Oh, thank God,' she breathed and stumbled up to fly into his arms.

'Feeling better?'

Tallitha closed her eyes. 'You're always saying that to me,' she said huskily. 'And feeding me restorative drinks,' she added with an attempt at wryness as she sipped another brandy on the rocks—the same brandy. 'Yes, I'm feeling better. Sorry.'

His arm tightened around her. They were sitting side by side on the bed against the upholstered cushions, she with her head on his shoulder and her knees curled up, her glass held in both hands because from time to time she couldn't help trembling stupidly.

They sat in silence for a while and he lifted his hand to play with her hair. I could die like this, quite happily, she thought. Only I can't, of course. And if I don't do something soon, he's going to get the wrong . . . the *right* impression.

She swallowed and sat up. 'You mustn't think . . . I mean I was so happy for Diana. Perhaps if I didn't have a stupid, dumb bird who won't talk to me I . . .' She trailed off and coloured, thinking, talk of stupid and dumb, what a dumb thing to say.

'Tallitha,'—he removed her glass which she was holding convulsively and put it down—'come back.'

'No,' she whispered and managed to glint a faint smile at him. 'You've already had to go to lengths far beyond the call of duty on account of me. I mean, even coming here on Christmas Day with presents for us all, without having to deal with hysterics! It was the nicest thing to do. Did she . . . did she like the dress? Your niece?'

He didn't answer immediately, just watched her

until she turned away awkwardly and went to get up. Then he put out a hand and pulled her back, right back against him with his arm around her. 'She loved it,' he said. 'So did my sister and everyone else who was there. In fact if you decided to become a couturier for very young ladies, I could put enough business your way to last quite some time.'

'I'm glad she liked it.'

'But I didn't come here as a duty,' he went on in that same quiet, different voice that was puzzling her slightly. 'I came because I wanted to. And now,' he slid his fingers through her hair, 'I find there's something else I want to do. Look at me, Tallitha.'

She raised her face mutely.

'This,' he said, and kissed her very gently on the lips. 'And this.' He slid his fingers down the slender column of her neck and up again to cup her cheek, and kissed her lips again lingeringly.

'Oh no,' she said on a breath, slowly, disbelievingly, and started to tremble all over again. 'No, you don't have to . . .'

She felt him smile and heard him say, 'I wanted to do it once before, only I didn't quite recognise what it was I wanted at the time. I think I told you you reminded me of something, that you were a mystery lady. But it was this I was thinking of, I discovered. How sweet it would be to kiss you.'

He did just that, very gently, very expertly, coaxingly until, from stunned passivity then a tremor of panicky resistance, she was kissing him back as she'd never kissed before.

It was quite dark when he raised his head at last, and she lay back against his arm breathing erratically, scanning the pale glimmer of his face anxiously. And perhaps he needed to see what was in her eyes, because he put out a hand gropingly and switched on the little alabaster lamp.

She blinked and went to hide her face in his shoulder but he stopped her with a hand on her chin.

'Don't,' he murmured, cupping her cheek again. 'Let's be honest about this. Did you mind? Did you hate it?'

She closed her eyes.

'Tallitha?'

'Oh, no,' she whispered.

'Look at me then.'

Her eyelashes fluttered up and her eyes were huge and very green.

'But you're shocked all the same,' he said wryly. 'Why?'

'I . . .' It was barely a thread of sound and she licked her lips. 'I just don't see how this could have happened,' she said unevenly.

'Do you know, it's funny you should say that. Because do you know when I unravelled the mystery lady bit? When you said that what Les had implied about us was not true and never could be true. I found myself thinking, oh yes it could, quite easily.'

She winced and a flood of colour stained her cheeks.

He watched it then he added soberly, 'What I meant was, you seemed so certain I could never find you . . . desirable.'

'I was.'

'Then you were wrong.' He traced the outline of her mouth, his lids lowered as he seemed to be concentrating intently on what he was doing. Then he looked up and his dark blue eyes smiled into hers.

Tallitha stared up at him, dazedly and with a question pounding her brain: But what about Heather Wentworth? What about Heather? What about . . .

But the answer followed hard on the heels of the question in the form of another question. Are desirable and *lovable* necessarily the same thing? Lovable as in the one love of your life, the one you really want but can't have . . .

'Do . . . do you know what I think?' she heard herself saying tremulously then. 'I think that for you I'm another Sonia. No,' she put a finger to his lips as he started to speak, 'I don't mind. It's *really* funny, because I should probably mind dreadfully, but I don't. What I would mind was if you went away and left me now because I've known for a little while that . . . that I'd like you to think of me this way. It's a real miracle, you know, for me.' Her voice trailed off huskily and it was with a sense of shock, but truth in her heart, that she knew she wouldn't recall her words if it were possible. Knew that she was setting the seal on wrecking her career as his secretary and one day, quite soon possibly, exposing herself to more loneliness than ever before. And knew that it didn't seem to matter.

He said, with a frown in his eyes, 'Tallitha . . .'

'Now don't argue with me, Mr Gilmour!' she warned impishly but then a wary seriousness came to her eyes and she said in a low shaken voice, 'I want you to teach me how to love and live again. I don't want you to make any promises to me or feel you have to worry about me. Please . . .'

'If you're thinking of Heather,' he began at last.

'You don't have to explain, I understand.'

He looked at her with a gleam of exasperation in his eyes but his lips twitching. 'How could I have forgotten how stubborn you can be? Are you trying to offer me an affair with no strings attached, and so on?'

'Yes. And I won't settle for anything less. You did

say let's be honest. What did you have in mind really?'

'Really?' he said slowly. 'I had in mind kissing you for two reasons—the one I told you, and because I really wanted to comfort you, and because I really care about you.'

'There you are, you see,' she whispered. '*I* jumped the gun, not you!'

'No! Tallitha . . .' But he was laughing down at her. '*You're* impossible!'

'Well, that's a change!' She smiled back up at him. 'But I'm also serious. No strings, no regrets afterwards, but because we *like* each other very much, and care, and sometimes, for different reasons, need some comfort. That's the way I would like it to be.'

An expression she couldn't decipher flickered in his eyes but it was gone almost immediately. And he said, at last, 'So be it. If you're very sure?'

'I am.'

She woke up the next morning with a curious thought on her mind—that Christmas, this Christmas anyway, had produced not one but two miracles.

And her mind roamed backwards then as she moved her cheek against Miles Gilmour's smooth, muscled chest and turned her head to lay her lips on his skin.

Back to where she'd run out of words last night and been paralysed with shyness after declaring herself so boldly, been suddenly afflicted with a horrible bout of nerves. But of course he'd known, as he'd always seemed to know so much about her, and he'd said with a glinting smile and his hands gentle on her face again, 'We should celebrate first. After all, we've come such a long way since we first . . . ran into each other.'

'I've got a nearly full bottle of wine. And a mountain of turkey we could eat, too. But I suppose you've had enough turkey for one day.'

'I only ever eat turkey once a year, so that I can eat it in one form of another for a couple of days without getting bored. That's a contradiction in terms, isn't it? What I mean is, I only eat it over Christmas.'

'Oh, I knew that!'

'That's because you're brighter than average, Miss Jones!'

'No.'

'Prettier then?'

'No.'

'Something then?'

'Maybe hungrier. I didn't eat much lunch.'

He'd laughed. 'Desperate, then.'

So they'd eaten cold turkey and cold Christmas pudding, and finished the wine and then sipped brandy while they'd listened to records—her motley collection, which ranged from Bob Marley to Beethoven.

And afterwards he'd sat on the floor leaning back against the bed with her in his lap, and they'd kissed again and then he'd started to undress her very slowly and he'd touched the velvety pink tips of her small round breasts, and she'd trembled and sighed and pressed her face into his shoulder at the wonder of it.

And the monsoon rain had hammered down creating the effect of a cocoon, insulating them from everything but his patient, tender lovemaking and her tears of happiness and delight.

'I didn't really believe it could be like that.'

'I know.'

She'd been lying against the length of him on her side with his arm around her, her head on his shoulder.

'For that matter,' he'd said then, 'neither did I.'

And he had turned to kiss the top of her head and slide his other arm around her.

'You don't have to say that,' she whispered.

'I meant it.'

'But . . .'

'You know, I did think,' he interrupted her gravely tilting her chin so that she had to look up into his eyes, 'that having you here at my mercy with not a stitch of clothing on your trim, gorgeous little body, might render you less argumentative, Tallitha Jones. But it seems I was wrong.'

A smile curved her lips. But she said then, equally gravely, 'It's not that I'm argumentative, just honest. But it was a lovely compliment all the same.'

'Oh well, I'll just have to prove to you that I was deadly serious then.'

'How?'

'Wouldn't you like to know?' he teased.

'Yes—No. I can't think of any way you could, anyway.'

'Which just goes to show how little you know, my dear Miss Jones,' he said a little mockingly, but kissed the tip of her nose. 'It's quite simple. I'll just have to keep on making love to you, night and day—and don't think I wouldn't do it!—until that argumentative, painfully honest, stubborn mind of yours gets the idea loud and clear, until you say to yourself, well, he wouldn't keep wanting to do it, would he, unless it's a bit special for him, too?'

'Oh,' she looked up at him with tears in her eyes, 'you do and say the nicest things sometimes.'

He stared down at her tears for a moment then pulled her closer. 'Just you wait,' he murmured into her hair. 'Just you wait . . .'

She went to sleep with those words in her mind.

*   *   *

But now, the next morning, she was thinking of miracles. Of Tallitha Jones reborn—at the hands of Miles Gilmour, the *last* person . . .

She sat up suddenly, clutching the sheet, then flinched and looked back to see if she'd woken him. But he was breathing deeply and evenly and she took the opportunity to look her fill. In sleep he looked graver than he often did awake, to her at least, but relaxed as she'd never seen him, with the force of that intelligent, sometimes cutting personality tamed for a while. And he was beautiful; pale skinned, long limbed, with wide, smooth shoulders, and some dark hair on his chest that she wanted to put out a hand and touch. But she didn't want to wake him; he was so sleek and beautiful. And she discovered she had sudden tears in her eyes because of it.

So she eased herself out of bed, glanced out of the window to see that it was still raining, and decided she would have a bath and then make breakfast.

She closed the communicating door and ran the bath and flung in great handfuls of the bubble bath that had been Amanda's Christmas present until the bath was all but obscured by foam and the bathroom filled with the fragrance of it. She tied her hair on top of her head with a green ribbon and stepped into the foamy water with a sigh of pleasure.

She soaked for about ten minutes, trying to think about the enormity of what had happened, about the way she had come to such a momentuous decision so . . . well, calmly almost. But in fact she had difficulty concentrating on those things because it was the state of her body that she really wanted to think about, she found. Trim and gorgeous, he'd said, and as she remembered it she sat up with a tremor and watched fascinated as the foam slid off her breasts.

It must have been a sixth sense that made her turn

towards the door, because the roof of the bathroom was an old tin one and the rain was hammering down, drowning out everything else.

Miles was standing in the doorway wearing only his trousers, still undone at the waistband, and with his arms folded across his chest, watching her intently. Her lips parted in surprise and she flushed.

He straightened slowly and came over to the bath and held a hand down to her.

She stood up slowly, her expression beneath a damp halo of auburn curls a little uncertain, and he watched, still holding her hand as the foam slid all the way down her gleaming body, clinging in little patches here and there. Then he looked up at last and she couldn't read his eyes at all.

He said, 'I hope you've got some more bubbles.'

'Yes I have, but . . .'

'Because these are going to go flat.' He lifted her hand and she stepped out of the bath and he let her go then and reached for a towel and wrapped it sarong-wise under her arms, which she raised obediently, but still with an uncertain look in her eyes.

And suddenly he smiled. 'You're going to pay the penalty now, that's what's going to happen.'

'For what?' she whispered.

'For getting up without telling me, for leaving me alone in a cold bed, for being so lovely and smelling so nice, for having such beautiful skin and such pretty breasts and,' he picked her up in his arms, 'for making me want you very much, quite without trying, I'm sure.'

'Oh!'

'Mmm. I did warn you, I think.'

She wound her arms round his neck and buried her face in his shoulder. And thought, no, no one warned

me, but I suspected that as a lover you would be . . .
like a dream come true. Only I didn't suspect even
half of it . . .

'I'm still a bit wet,' she whispered when he laid her
on the bed and unwrapped the towel.

'All the more delicious,' he said lazily and lay down
beside her. 'What's wrong?' he added with a suddenly
alert look as he trailed his fingers down the outline of
her thigh.

'Nothing. What do you mean?' she said after a
moment.

'You look very serious.'

Do I? Do I? She repeated the mental question with
a curious sense of foreboding. But *I* made the rules,
she thought next, and I know I have to stick to them,
however hard.

'I feel serious,' she said very quietly, and turned her
head to kiss the upper part of his arm as it lay across
her body. 'It's a serious business this, isn't it? And
anyway, I'm always serious first thing in the
morning—one of *those* kind of people,' she warned,
but with a smile trembling on her lips.

'Oh, I see.' He gathered her very close. 'Then let's
make serious love,' he said gravely.

But in fact it turned out to be the same as the night
before, joyous, sensuous, tender—lovely.

'Oh!' she said under her breath. 'Oh, oh . . .'

'Yes,' he agreed with an effort, holding her
arched, quivering body against him very hard. And
later, when they were still at last, he said with a
smile in his voice and eyes, 'Give me a serious lover
any day.'

She giggled.

'I thought you said . . .' he started

'It doesn't last long.'

'Good. Tallitha, have you ever been to New South Wales?'

'No. Why?'

'It mightn't be raining there.'

'Well, it is a big place,' she agreed solemnly.

'I was thinking about just over the border—about three hours' drive away. I have friends who have a holiday home at Cabarita, but they've gone to America for three months and left me with a key and an open invitation to use it whenever I like.'

She stirred in his arms and said after a while, 'But didn't you have plans for the holidays?'

'Nothing irrevocable.'

'I . . . There's Mason.'

'Mason,' he said thoughtfully. 'I know, we'll take him with us!'

'But . . .'

'Don't you want to come away with me, Tally-ho?' he asked reproachfully.

'If you're sure . . .'

He kissed the top of her head. 'Never surer, lady,' he said laconically. 'And anyway,' he added, 'I'm not one of those lazy, slothful people who lie in bed in the mornings, like some people I know.'

'Oh! You were the one . . .'

About four hours later, Tallitha grinned across at Miles Gilmour as they approached a modern, rough brick house that was built into a rocky headland—their destination apparently. 'I thought you said it wasn't raining in New South Wales?'

Miles grimaced at the lowering clouds that stretched across the magnificent vista of ocean before them, all the way to the horizon. 'I said it mightn't be. Like it?' He pulled up in the steep driveway before the garage door.

Tallitha looked at the house, at the marvellous aspect—the beach below was white and clean and went for miles in both directions. 'It's lovely. And I don't care about the rain,' she added softly.

He leant across and kissed her.

Inside the house, she couldn't help wondering what Miles's friend's proper home was like if this was his holiday home, because it was lovely—beautifully decorated with every mod. con., and, from every room, views of the sea and beach, and a marvellously private terrace. They chose a bedroom, not the main bedroom because she said she wouldn't feel right about that. Then they went up to the village—it was little more than that, a few shops and a pub—and laid in supplies.

That was when Tallitha got the first intimation that Miles was planning to stay longer than the Christmas break.

'We've got enough for a month!' she said laughingly.

But all he said was, 'Being at the seaside makes you hungry, didn't you know?'

'Well—no. I've never been to the seaside properly, not to stay. But I still think . . .'

'Never?' he interrupted with his eyebrows raised.

'I never saw the sea until I was eighteen,' she confessed. 'And Brisbane isn't really seaside unless you go right out, is it? But I have been to Surfers' Paradise for the day a couple of times.'

'Like it?'

'Surfers' or the sea?'

He laughed. 'Both.'

'I like Surfers'. And I love the sea. Only I'm a bit frightened of being in it,' she said ruefully.

But he didn't look askance, as she half expected, just took her hand and pressed it. 'Trust me,' he said.

*   *   *

Many months later she could still remember every detail of that holiday at Cabarita, and knew that it would probably be impossible to forget, even when she was very old.

How could one forget? How could you ever forget the way the sun shone the day after they arrived and how the sea glittered and danced beneath a blue, blue sky. Or the way Miles had taken her hand and coaxed her into it little by little and held her so close afterwards because her heart was thumping with fright.

'We'll take it slowly,' he'd said.

And she'd marvelled at how fearless he was, how he swam right out and surfed back in on the waves, and she'd decided to be much braver the next time.

How could you forget being lazy with sun, sea and wine, after lunch that same day, and being led into the cool, tiled guest bedroom and being put to bed like a child for an afternoon nap. She had showered after coming up from the beach and exchanged her yellow cotton bikini—bought two years ago for her first trip to Surfers' Paradise and worn only once since—for a pair of bright pink shorts and a white blouse. And they'd made lunch together, cold meat and tomatoes and thick, crusty brown bread, and drunk a rosé from a cask Miles had bought, saying that it was cheap but had the advantage of being on tap if you only wanted a glass now and then.

It was after lunch that she'd yawned three times and found she could barely keep her eyes open.

'I'm sorry—I don't know why I'm so sleepy,' she'd mumbled in the bedroom, fumbling with the buttons of her blouse.

'The seaside does that to you, too,' he'd said and added, 'Let me.'

His fingers had been cool on her bare skin as he'd

slid the blouse off, and she'd woken up a bit and looked up at him uncertainly. But he'd been studying her shoulders and breasts and he turned her round absently and then back again. 'We'll have to watch that superfine skin. It's a bit pink. Sore?'

'No, I put plenty of lotion on.'

'Good. Take your shorts off and hop in.'

'Are you . . . I mean . . .'

'No, I'm going to find another bed.'

'I'll probably wake up a bit if . . . you'd like me to,' she said, feeling shy and awkward.

He'd smiled. 'I'd love you to, but later perhaps. I think you need a good sleep. It's been a rather momentous couple of days, I think.'

'Yes,' she'd whispered and smiled back sleepily. And two minutes after he'd left her she'd fallen asleep between the deliciously cool sheets.

It had been late afternoon when she woke and she had lain for a while drowsily re-orientating herself, and wishing that this paradise could last for ever. But tomorrow they would be heading back to Brisbane, she knew.

She'd heard Miles talking when she got up and, following the sound of his voice, had wandered into the study in time to see him put the phone down.

'Good evening!' he'd teased.

'Sorry,' she'd said ruefully. 'Fancy sleeping this kind of holiday away!'

He'd reached for her. 'Never mind, we have plenty of time.' He'd kissed her hair. 'Another two weeks, anyway.'

'Two?' She'd looked up at him wide-eyed.

'Mmm. I've just arranged it on the phone.'

'But . . .'

'But what? I told you it was always difficult to get anything done at this time of year, didn't I?'

'Yes, but . . . I mean, what about Janet, for one thing?'

He'd laughed and she'd coloured under his amused scrutiny. 'Well, you *know* what I mean,' she'd said wryly. 'I love the thought of two whole weeks, but . . .'

'For one thing, you were right about Miss Janet Laidley,' he'd interrupted. 'In fact I'll go further. She has the makings of a great secretary and will probably one day make someone a very managing wife.'

'How do you know all this?'

'Well, you warned me, didn't you? and after you left on Christmas Eve and I was wondering how to get rid of everyone else, she took command. She produced coffee and sobered us all up, and then packed us off in no time at all. It was very cleverly done and, for now and ever more, I have great faith in Janet.'

'Oh.'

'Yes. Any more objections, Miss Jones?'

She'd grimaced. 'Can't think of any.'

'Then let's go for a swim.'

The two weeks flew by.

Two golden weeks of mostly perfect weather during which they swam—Tallitha with increasing confidence—fished, walked, drove around the beautiful Northern Rivers area of New South Wales, and slept.

They also talked, sometimes far into the night lying under the stars on the loungers on the terrace, sometimes in bed, holding hands. And afterwards she sometimes thought she'd talked more in those two weeks than in her entire life—that it was as if he'd tapped a secret well within her.

And they made love whenever the mood took them. And she discovered that she was more ardent and passionate than she thought she could ever be, responsive and joyful, sometimes playful, sometimes so moved that tears were the only fitting response.

Like the night of the New Year's Eve dance at the local pub.

'Shall we go?'

'Why not?'

Tallitha donned a pretty cotton dress that matched her eyes, with a full skirt and a halter neck because Miles said it wouldn't be a very dressy occasion.

He was right. But it turned out to be a very lively one, and they danced until she was pink cheeked and breathless and ended up sitting with a group of very friendly strangers—that was until Tallitha, without quite knowing how, got involved in an argument with a man about nuclear arms.

'But isn't it senseless to go on stockpiling them and *testing* them,' she said heatedly. 'Somewhere on earth has got to suffer for that alone. And how can we guarantee that everyone is always going to be cool, calm and logical about it? That someone, some day, doesn't have a rush of blood and order the button to be pushed? You know, forgets the golden rule— they're *there* but they're not to be *used* except to menace the other side. And what about computer errors?'

Fortunately, as she and her antagonist were looking at each other rather hostilely—he was very much on the side of the deterrent effect of nuclear weapons— midnight struck, thereby effectively ending all arguments. And Miles took her in his arms and kissed her lingeringly.

'I think I'd like to go home now,' she said a little tremulously afterwards.

Miles looked at her interrogatively but said simply, 'All right.'

But once home and getting ready for bed, she found herself feeling restless and nervy and she brushed her hair for an extra long time, and fiddled with her short white nightgown until Miles put out the light and said, 'Come to bed, Tally-ho! Even redheaded firebrands need to sleep.'

She had to grin ruefully as she climbed in beside him. 'You're right,' she said into his shoulder. 'The silly thing is, I really don't remember how it all started. What a topic for New Year's Eve! But I do . . . I do worry about it.'

'Most of us do, I think,' he said quietly and stroked her hair.

She lay still for a time but realised that something else had mingled with her original feeling of distress, something that had come with his New Year kiss and the new year itself. And to distract herself she began to touch him lovingly but a little jerkily, as if her strained nerves were very close to the surface.

'Tallitha,' he said after a time, 'relax . . .'

'I . . . can't,' she whispered. 'I don't know what's wrong with me.'

'Yes you can—just lie still.'

It was very quiet in the house on the headland, with only the faint sound of surf to be heard. A ribbon of moonlight lay across the bedroom floor, silvering the outline of the bed.

And Tallitha lay on it, listening tensely to the surf, wanting to cry or wanting to die, she wasn't sure which, because she was burdened in a way she'd never been burdened before with a sense of doom and a sense of loss so great it was like the ocean below in its infinity.

But Miles moved and began to stroke her body until finally he brought to her a gradual softening and when he turned her on to her side and into his arms, she came obediently and with a little sigh of relief. And she lay there, quietening within, with the empty spaces receding as his hands continued caressing her, the nape of her neck, the small of her back, the curve of her bottom.

And with the quietening came a sense of need, not urgent as it sometimes was, not with a lovely, laughing feeling of tenderness, not with gratitude as it sometimes still was for his understanding; but a deeper need to give herself to him completely while she was still able to—to imprint some little part of her on him, some part of her spirit, she thought dimly.

Whatever it was, and perhaps after all it was gratitude, she realised just before falling asleep in his arms with tears on her lashes, it wasn't quite like any time they'd made love before. Because even in the morning, when she woke to find him already awake and watching her in the early sunlight, the impact of it was still with them. She could see it in the gravity of his dark blue eyes and feel it as he reached out after a while and cupped her cheek—his very own signal to her that he understood.

She turned her head slightly to kiss his palm, his wrist. But she closed her eyes, suddenly afraid of him understanding completely. And she was flooded with a sense of wariness and warning that told her to be careful, that she was stepping outside the rules . . .

They spent New Year's Day quietly which was what Tallitha desperately needed—to get her act together, as she thought of it. To get back to her cheerful self. To the Tallitha Jones who reached out for this so surprisingly, and damn the consequences; to herself.

As the second week drew to a close, she thought she'd succeeded. There had certainly been no more attacks of nerves or whatever it had been. And yet, on their second last day, she noticed that Miles was quieter. Late in the afternoon he stood on the terrace for a long time, staring out to sea with his hands shoved into his pockets.

She went out to him eventually and stood beside him silently, thinking he hadn't even heard her, but after a few minutes he put an arm round her shoulder without looking and said, 'Hello, Curlytop.'

'Hello. What are you thinking about?'

He didn't answer for a moment. Then she thought she heard him sigh and he said, 'How beautiful it is. And about . . .'

She knew with an instinctive shrinking that he'd been going to say, about us, but the phone rang and they looked at each other in surprise.

'That's got to be Rathdowney, MacPherson & Gilmour,' he said wryly. 'No one else knows I'm here.'

It was. Tallitha went into the kitchen to start dinner, but she could hear Miles on the phone. It was Hugo Rathdowney he was talking to.

Then the phone was put down sharply and he came looking for her. She was peeling potatoes under the tap and he leant against the kitchen counter and said, 'All hell's broken loose, I'm afraid.'

'Oh?'

'Yes—by the way, don't peel any more—it's the shopping centre. One of the major building-contractors has gone bankrupt overnight. Which will mean calling for new tenders and a delay in starting work, and that's going to wreak havoc with everyone else's schedules. Would you mind very much if we went home tonight?'

Tallitha reached for a tea-towel and dried her hands. 'No. Of course not.'

'Not that there's anything I can do tonight,' he said savagely, 'but . . .'

'I know,' she interrupted soothingly. 'But you can start first thing in the morning. I'm really sorry this has happened after you worked so hard.'

'And you,' he said with a sudden smile quirking his lips. 'Tallitha,' he added with a new expression in his eyes, but the phone started to ring again. 'Hell!' he said, instead of what he'd been going to say. 'Hugo doesn't panic easily, but he's manifesting serious signs of it now. I bet that's him again.'

It was, and Tallitha started to pack hurriedly. In fact they left so quickly she forgot Mason, and had to run back for him. 'Just one thing,' she said breathlessly, climbing into the car again. 'I was really going to polish the place up tomorrow. It's clean, but . . .'

'Don't worry. They have a cleaning lady who lives in the village. She comes in once a fortnight when the place is empty.'

'Oh.'

'Look, I'm sorry about the mad haste,' he went on, reversing down the drive very fast, 'but I said I'd call in and see Hugo this evening. We'll only make Brisbane by about half-past eight as it is.'

'I don't mind,' she assured him, but clutched the seatbelt as the car spurted forward.

He glinted a dark blue glance at her and slackened off slightly. 'You're right. It would be better to arrive without a speeding ticket.'

But although he kept within the letter of the law, it was a fast though competent drive to Brisbane and they didn't talk much. And he turned off the freeway much earlier than one would to go to the suburb of Ashgrove.

She said, as he nosed the car into the underground car park of his apartment block, 'I'll get a taxi home.'

'No, you won't.'

'But you could be very late,' she objected.

'And you can have a bath and go to bed if you want to,' he said, removing both their bags from the boot. 'You bring Mason.'

'Miles . . .'

But he was off, striding towards the lift, and she had to run to keep up with him, which annoyed Mason immensely and scattered birdseed in their wake.

She tried again in the lift, 'Miles, I think I ought to go home.'

'What for?'

'Well . . .'

But the lift had stopped and they stepped out and he had his key ready. 'In you go,' he commanded, and added with a grin, 'I gather Mason is a slow mover as well as a slow thinker, from the outraged noises he's making. I'm going to have a quick shower. Make yourself at home.'

'Miles . . .' She sighed as he disappeared, and she put Mason down on the floor. After a moment or two he stopped fluttering dementedly around his cage to sit in a corner and sulk.

She sat down herself, dispirited and worried.

'What's the matter, Tallitha?'

She jumped and looked up at Miles as he came towards her, buttoning up his shirt and with his hair damp and hastily brushed.

'I . . . I still think I ought to go home,' she stammered.

'And I think you should stay the night with me,' he said, reaching down and drawing her to her feet. 'For one very good reason,' he went on with a glint of determination but also amusement in his dark blue eyes. 'So that I can formally and properly ask you to marry me, Tallitha. And so that you can formally and properly accept.'

CHAPTER SEVEN

TALLITHA stared at the front door of the apartment with her hand to her lips.

She had said nothing since Miles Gilmour had proposed to her informally, mainly because of sheer shock but also because he hadn't given her a chance to say anything. He'd led her by the hand into the kitchen, rummaged in the freezer and produced a frozen pizza and a frozen apple pie, apologised with a wry grin for not being able to feed her better, shown her the microwave oven and then taken her into his arms.

'Don't look so stunned, Mrs Gilmour-to-be,' he'd teased, and had kissed her. 'I'll be back as soon as I can. But go to bed if you want to.'

'You're impossible,' Tallitha whispered to the closed front door. 'Impossible . . . and I was afraid this was going to happen. So I'll just have to sit down and think it all out. Think of how I'm going to say no. Because I *have* thought it all out, haven't I? Time and time again, even when I tried not to, when I pretended to myself I was just going to live in the present, hour to hour, day to day.'

But perhaps it would be better just to *go* home, she thought shakily. Only, go home and what? Hide? Like a rabbit? Oh, God! What am I going to do?

What she did, after a long time, was heat up the pizza, only to eat a few bites of a slice. Then she made herself a cup of coffee, black because there was no milk, and wandered around disconsolately with it.

Finally, she took part of his advice. She had a bath in his sumptuous sunken bath, and because for better or worse she was obviously going to be there for what remained of the night, she put on a nightgown and her robe. Then she wandered back into the lounge and switched on the television and curled up in a chair opposite. But the effort to concentrate was too great and she fell asleep. The last thing she'd wanted to do . . .

She woke up in his arms.

'Miles?' she murmured sleepily.

'Mmm. It's all right. I'm just taking you to bed, which is where you should have put yourself in the first place, Curlytop. Can you switch on the light?'

'The . . . Oh. Yes.' She put out a hand over his shoulder and pressed the wall switch. The central light sprang on and he carried her over to the bed, a double bed with a silky coral spread that matched the curtains and contrasted well with the pale grey carpet.

She blinked dazedly as he set her gently down on the bed and he laughed at her. 'Here.' He pulled the cover back on one side, and the sheet. 'Move over.'

She did after a moment and submitted warily to having her robe taken off and being laid back against the pillows and covered up like a child. Then he switched on the lamp on the other side of the bed and walked to the door to switch off the main light. Immediately the large, elegant room became invested with mysterious shadows, and the view from the terrace beyond the sliding glass doors brightened, as if the lights of Brisbane had been turned up.

He sat down on the bed and pulled off his shoes. Then he stood up and pulled his keys and money and some slips of paper, which he glanced at cursorily, from his trouser pockets and put them on a lovely cedar chest-of-drawers.

As Tallitha watched, she thought with a sudden pang, I could have this for the rest of my life, this ritual of going to bed together, not necessarily for sex but still just as intimate. In the good times and the bad, I could always watch the way he takes his shoes off first, then empties his pockets, then his shirt. She bit her lip and spoke without thinking.

'What . . .?'

'Well?'

He'd turned his head to ask her the question and their words clashed. He raised an eyebrow at her.

'W-what time is it?'

'About half-past twelve,' he said without consulting his watch. 'A bit later than I anticipated.' He pulled his shirt off over his head as if impatient with all the buttons and said again, 'Well?'

Her heart shrank because she recognised his mood. This was the Miles Gilmour who dealt in practicalities and realities, who didn't essentially believe in beating about the bush, not even in this.

'I . . . I think we should talk about it in the morning,' she said.

'There won't be time in the morning, Tallitha. But anyway there's not much to talk about, is there? A simple yes will do it.'

'Miles . . .'

He sat down on the bed beside her. 'What else did you plan to say? I gather you have something else in mind. I could see it in your eyes as soon as you woke up properly,' he said grimly.

She took a breath. 'Well, perhaps, but I really don't think this is a good time to . . . You must be tired, for one thing.'

'My dear Tallitha,' he said through his teeth, and hauled her up by her shoulders, 'there's never going to be a better time. Especially if you're planning to say no.'

'Oh,' she gasped, and tried to wrench herself free as his fingers dug painfully into her flesh. And suddenly she was furious. 'Listen to me, Miles Gilmour,' she hissed, 'you can't deal with me like a business proposition, cut and dried and *we must sort this out now because there's no time in the morning*—it's taken up with other business, isn't it? But as a matter of fact I understand about the other business, which is why of *course* it's not a good time to talk about getting married. Any fool could see that. And will you let me *go*!'

'No,' he said briefly, but relaxed his grip slightly. 'And that's not the point, although thank you for being so understanding.' His dark blue look was supremely ironic. 'The point is, you're trying to evade the issue, which strikes me as ludicrous. For example, were you planning to sleep with me tonight and say to me tomorrow, sorry, Miles, but I can't marry you? Doesn't that strike you as ludicrous?'

'You didn't give me any choice!'

'Maybe I had an inkling of this,' he said savagely. 'I wonder why?' he mocked.

'Because you know very well it's not the right thing for us,' she whispered.

'No I don't,' he countered swiftly. 'I know the opposite. I know we've been as close as two people can get lately. I also know,' he smiled unpleasantly, 'about your bloody stubborn-mindedness from past experience!'

'*You* . . .' She went as white as a sheet from rage, and her eyes glittered like emeralds as she lunged at him furiously.

He let her go, but only to ward her off quite easily and with a totally dispassionate expression, which infuriated her even more. But when she uncurled one fist, he caught her wrists in a grasp of steel, and drawled, 'I was remarkably understanding the last time you did that to me, Tallitha. I doubt if I'd be so again.' And he pulled her into his lap with one arm around her, his other hand still clamped around her wrists.

She lay panting and dishevelled, her eyes still glittering with anger, her mouth set mutinously.

'All right,' he said, when her breathing became less erratic. 'Tell me why it's not the right thing for us. Tell me you haven't enjoyed the last two weeks, haven't felt comfortable, haven't felt *right*. Tell me what the hell you're going to do with yourself now. Apply for an urgent transfer to Travel and walk past me primly with downcast eyes whenever we chance to meet, as if we never lay in each other's arms and made sometimes extremely passionate love? Or did you plan to go on being my secretary and be content with a quick one now and then between dictating sessions? But you've come a long way in the last two weeks, and *that* would be hard to imagine as satisfactory.'

Tallitha stared up at him and felt a red tide of colour rise from the base of her throat. She closed her eyes and willed it to go away but it didn't; it fed, instead, on the images he had created, and stained her cheeks and made her shudder, and she burst into tears. 'I . . . I hate you!' she wept.

'No you don't,' he countered, and looked down grimly at her quivering lips. And in an instant, she realised what he was going to do and she twisted in his arms, but it was no good, he was far too strong for her.

It was a kiss that left her gasping and clutching at

him fearfully, her eyes hurt and dazed and full of uncomprehending reproach.

'Oh, *hell*,' he said with a sudden frown of pain. 'I'm sorry. Don't look like that—you of all people must know I've got a terrible temper.' And he held her close and rocked her in his arms until she stopped shaking. Then he kissed her again, stilling her little spurt of panic with gentle hands, holding her carefully and delicately as if she might break, until she relaxed and surrendered her mouth with a husky little sound of despair and desire.

Later, when they were lying side by side, he picked up her hand and threaded his fingers between hers, and said, in an oddly strained voice, 'How can I convince you it is the right thing for us? I know,'—his fingers tightened on hers as they moved convulsively— 'I know what you're thinking—were thinking. About being another kind of Sonia to me, about Heather, and probably a whole lot of other things that have never even occurred to me. But that's all in the past now . . . Don't you see?'

That same afternoon, Tallitha looked round her bed-sitter as if through new eyes. And why not? she thought. It's part of another life and one I'm about to dismantle now that I've committed myself to becoming Mrs Miles Gilmour.

A tremor ran through her and she wished suddenly and desperately that Miles was with her, to still her fears and uncertainties as only he could. But Miles had gone to work, and come home to his apartment at lunchtime with the news that he had to go to Melbourne—the home base of the bankrupt company—he wasn't sure for how long. He'd tried to persuade her to stay on at the apartment. At least I can reach you on the phone, he'd said. It was one point she'd stood firm on, though.

She had pointed out that she was going to have to make arrangements about her flat and her furniture anyway, and this would be a good time to do it, while he was away.

'Just so long as you don't change your mind,' he'd said in the end, because they were running late as it was for his flight. 'Promise me?'

'I promise,' she'd whispered.

He'd dropped her off on his way to the airport and his last words had been, 'You do understand—I know I was rather scathing about it last night, but you do understand about this, don't you, Tallitha?'

'Yes I do, really. Don't worry about me.'

She came back to the present with a sigh and thought, this is no good. If I'm going to go through with this, I have to put all my fears and uncertainties behind me because I can't expect him to be by my side holding my hand all the time. Perhaps I should take them out *now* and look them all in the face when he isn't with me, calmly and without the . . . without what he does to me.

She laid her head back and closed her eyes, and thought suddenly, it's not that I expect him to love me the way he loved Heather. I know this has to be something different for him, but will it be special enough to make him forget her? Will . . . No, I won't think of that.

But in the end she couldn't help herself from thinking of all the rumours associated with Miles and Heather. Had they had an affair while Heather was married to Hayden Wentworth? Would she perhaps be placing herself in a position similar to Hayden Wentworth's? And could she still love Miles Gilmour if that were the case?

'But the thing is, I don't believe they did,' she said out aloud and with a curious sense of conviction that surprised her a little and caused her to ask herself why she didn't believe it? Miles had never denied it, although he hadn't confirmed it either. On the occasion they'd discussed it, he'd left it up to her to make her own decision. 'And it seems I have,' she whispered, 'subconsciously perhaps, but all the same. I've made it. Why, though? Wishful thinking?'

She opened her eyes and looked around the room and found the answer right there, where he had first made love to her: I trust him, I've trusted his integrity for a long time now. If I hadn't I'd never have wanted to love him because, for me, that would have been making the same mistake again. Perhaps some people would say it's not logical but I can't help it. I do trust him not to betray me like that and, yes, with that sorted out, I somehow feel a whole lot more confident.

She sat up and reached absently for the pile of mail that had accumulated in her box. To her delight, there was a letter from Diana and it was full of good news. Her parents had insisted that she move back home, they were crazy about Amanda, they'd bought her a little car—Diana, not Amanda—and persuaded her to look around for a part-time job as a start to opening up her life again. And she went on to say how sad she was to have missed Tallitha on the day she and her father had come back to pick up her things, but that she hoped they would keep in touch and Tallitha would be able to go up and see them soon. You were the best friend I ever had, she finished.

The writing blurred as Tallitha blinked away some tears. 'And the same goes for you, Diana,' she murmured. But although she wanted to write back straight away, her notepaper was already packed. Well,

I'll have all the time in world anyway, she thought, and set about doing some more packing.

The next morning she received a telegram from Melbourne which said simply, 'Missing you already, Miles.'

She read it with her lips curving into a smile and a feeling of warmth and courage in her heart. Two hours later, just as the second-hand furniture dealer was leaving, another telegram arrived. It was the same delivery man and he said jovially, 'This is becoming a habit! Sign here, please.'

'It seems to be,' she agreed but thought, not Miles again, surely?

It wasn't. 'Please contact me immediately if at all possible. Signed Fortescue—Rathdowney, Mac-Pherson & Gilmour', Tallitha read, and stared at the form with parted lips.

Her first thought was that something had happened to Miles but, as her heart started to beat heavily, she realised they wouldn't be contacting *her* if it had, because they didn't even know, unless he'd told Miss Fortescue. But no, he wouldn't have done that, not in the midst of a crisis like this one.

'Well, there's only one way to find out,' she chided herself.

'Miss Fortescue, it's Tallitha Jones,' she said into the public phone down the road. 'I got your telegram.'

'Oh Tallitha!' Miss Fortescue's voice came down the wire rather eagerly. 'My dear girl, I do apologise for this and I didn't even know if you'd be home because you still have nearly a week of holiday left. But the thing is we're in a bit of a flat spin here.' She went on to explain why. 'And the other thing is, Mr Gilmour's in Melbourne,' she added, and paused for breath.

Tallitha started to say yes I know, but bit her tongue in time.

'And,' Miss Fortescue continued, 'Miss Laidley, who I must say has been coping rather well, has this very morning developed a mystery virus. A temperature and a raging headache, and we've had to send the poor girl home. Would you consider coming in to help us out? The thing is, you were in on the ground floor of this business, and so you'd be invaluable at the moment anyway. But of *course*, if you have plans . . .' Her voice faded away.

A jumble of thoughts shot through Tallitha's head. Should she? Would Miles mind? They simply hadn't had the time to discuss her resigning from Rathdowney, MacPherson & Gilmour but she'd assumed she wouldn't be going back. On the other hand, no one knew, obviously, and it *had* also occurred to her that she would be—if not invaluable—helpful in this situation.

'Miss Fortescue, I'll come in now if you like,' she said abruptly. 'Well, give me an hour or so.'

'Oh, thank you so much, Tallitha!' Miss Fortescue sounded really relieved. 'I can assure you Mr Gilmour will be *most* grateful to you. The other problem is, he's been away himself and he was back only for a few hours yesterday, and he left screeds of instructions which you will probably be better able to decipher than anyone.'

Miss Fortescue said again, 'Mr Gilmour will be most grateful to you, Tallitha,' when Tallitha arrived to find her manning the outer office. And she experienced a curious feeling of embarrassment as she murmured something a little incoherent in reply. It seemed a rather underhand thing to be doing. On the other hand, she didn't feel at all up to explaining the recent turn of events herself.

'Here are Miss Laidley's notes,' Miss Fortescue went on, 'and . . . I must say you're looking very well, Tallitha!' she exclaimed as if she'd suddenly noticed the faint golden bloom on Tallitha's skin, which was as close as she ever came to tanning.

'Thank you. I . . . I did go away for a while.'

'Funnily enough Mr Gilmour is quite tanned himself. But I don't suppose you know that he took off quite unexpectedly and had a holiday, too. Which,' she said conspiratorially, 'is probably a good thing. I can remember thinking before Christmas that he looked as if he needed one. Such a pity this has happened—it could undo all the good his holiday did him!' She directed Tallitha a rueful little grin, but Tallitha was spared any further embarrassment because the phone rang then, and from then on it was strictly business. Miss Fortescue stayed with her for an hour or so, going through Janet's notes with her and relaying Mr Rathdowney's instructions—he had also gone to Melbourne—on how the situation was to be handled with other sub-contractors who were naturally concerned about the delay there would be.

'Right, I think I've got it,' Tallitha said finally. 'Mainly a stalling brief, and anything I can't stall I pass on to Mr Seymour or Mr Jacobs, and in the meantime I get out all the tenders, contracts, etc., and get them over to the solicitors for re-assessment—that kind of thing.'

'That kind of thing' kept her flat out for the rest of the day, and she got to work early the next morning to cope with the backlog.

At about ten o'clock her phone rang. She barely had time to say anything into it when the voice on the end started to speak. 'Janet? It's Miles Gilmour here. Will you . . .'

'Miles!'

There was a moment's silence. Then, abruptly, '*Tallitha?*'

'Yes. Where are you?'

'Melbourne. What the hell are you doing there?'

'I . . . Janet's sick and Miss Fortescue got in touch with me and asked me to help out. I hope you don't mind, but they were in a bit of a mess.'

'Yes, I do mind,' he said in clipped tones. 'She should have consulted me first.'

'But she didn't know. Thank you for the telegram,' she said a little tremulously, wondering *why* he minded so much.

He said on a slightly softer note, 'How are you?'

'Fine . . .'

'I'm sorry—I didn't mean to bark. The thing is, I guess I didn't want you to be back in that environment again. In case it reactivates all your doubts, I suppose. Has it?'

'No,' she said softly. 'I'll never be able to think of you as my boss again.'

'You don't know how pleased I am to hear you say that. Well, I suppose it has its compensations. At least I can talk to you . . .'

They talked for about twenty minutes. She told him about Diana's letter, about the offer the furniture man had made her, which she thought was too low, and finally they talked about business. And just before he rang off he said, and she could just picture his eyes glinting wickedly, 'I imagine you'll think this is crazy of me in view of my earlier sentiments, but thank God you're there. At least I know *you'll* cope.'

'Why, thank you, Mr Gilmour,' she replied demurely, and they both rang off laughing.

It was only a few hours later that that secret well of warmth and laughter dried up—at the hands of a vitally attractive brunette who swept into the outer office on a wave of Joy and wearing the most beautiful swathed silk dress in muted shades of amber and toffee, delicate patterned stockings and very high, brown, alligator-skin shoes. She carried a matching alligator purse which she dumped on the desk unceremoniously as she said, 'What's this I hear about Miles being in Melbourne now?'

Tallitha blinked and the woman took a closer look at her and then smiled brilliantly. 'I know who you are,' she said, her dark blue eyes twinkling suddenly. 'Sorry for barging in on you like that but I thought that you were on holiday. You're his Miss Jones, aren't you? He's told me all about you—well, I forced it out of him when he said you were the creator of that marvellous dress he gave to Cassie for Christmas. I'm his sister.'

'Oh! I thought . . . How do you do?' Tallitha said somewhat dazedly.

'You thought we looked alike?'

'It's the eyes. Won't you sit down, Mrs . . . Er . . . Mr Gilmour *is* in Melbourne on business,' Tallitha said, rather flustered, and thinking inwardly, help!

'Well, I will,' his sister said. 'I'm really very cross about the whole business. He could have rung me—I mean it really wasn't my fault. And as for swearing Hugo to secrecy—what does he think I am?'

'I . . .'

'Don't have a clue what I'm talking about, I expect,' said Miles Gilmour's sister ruefully. 'I'm noted for that, I'm afraid; also for putting my foot into things, although . . . But anyway, I'm Susan, Susan Wentworth, for my sins—but please call me Susan.

After all we do have a common interest at heart, don't we? Your boss and my brother. How is he? Did he look—normal to you?'

'I . . . I . . . Well, yes,' Tallitha said helplessly.

'Hmm.' Susan Wentworth—*Wentworth?* Tallitha thought—looked pensive. Then she smiled her lovely warm smile again and said, 'By the way, I must thank you for that beautiful purse he gave me for Christmas. Yes, he confessed that you'd bought that, too. As for Cassie's dress, we were all in raptures over it and Heather—you might have met my sister-in-law, Heather Wentworth? Well Heather,' she went on as Tallitha nodded faintly, 'is expecting a baby and she's hoping for a girl and she was asking Miles if he thought you would consider making a christening robe—even if it's a boy! Did he ask you?'

'No, but . . .'

'Hasn't had the time, I suppose,' Susan said understandingly. 'Well!' She stood up, but the outer door opened and Miss Fortescue walked in; Susan Wentworth uttered a cry of delight and rose to embrace her.

'Frosty!' she said. 'They told me you might not be back for hours!'

'Well I am, and I heard you were asking for me,' Miss Fortescue said calmly but affectionately and with one eyebrow raised.

'It's Miles,' Susan said. 'I'm worried about him, although Miss Jones says he looks quite normal but you know how good he is at covering up . . . What's the matter?'

'Nothing,' Miss Fortescue replied, but she had in fact cast Tallitha a suddenly frowning look. 'Should we go into Miles's office?' she said then. 'I'm sure

Tallitha will excuse us.' And she ushered Susan Wentworth into the inner office and closed the door.

Tallitha stared at the door and discovered that her heart was beating erratically and her mouth was dry, and not only because what she was about to do was terribly unethical. All the same she got up and crossed the carpet to stand right outside the door. Perhaps being slammed so often had affected its fit, and certainly Susan's clear, cultivated voice helped, because she found she could hear quite well.

'It was all Rupert's idea,' Susan Wentworth was saying disgustedly. 'I told him it was a crazy idea but he said it had all gone on for too long, and that Hayden was his brother and that he was tired of *us* being like a family cut in two, especially with the baby on the way. And all because Heather, he said, was the only MacPherson he'd ever known who couldn't make up her mind. You know what Rupert's like, Frosty! He really believes families should stick together and I agree with him—I also agree it's getting awkward with the kids—you know the kind of things they're starting to ask—Don't Uncle Miles and Uncle Hayden like each other? Why don't they?'

Miss Fortescue murmured something.

'But to ask them all for Christmas Day and absolutely refuse to allow me to warn Miles—that's another of Rupert's pet theories, that one should put all one's squabbles behind one at Christmas and expect miracles.' Tallitha winced. 'Can you imagine what it was like?'

'Difficult,' Miss Fortescue pronounced.

'Oh well, no it wasn't actually,' Susan said. 'They behaved beautifully. They fell over themselves to carry on as if nothing was wrong. I mean Miles and Hayden chatted for ages about finance and God knows what. And as for Heather, well you know the effect she has on everyone, and now she's pregnant . . . But then you see, Miles left early and when I went out to say goodbye to him for a moment he looked tired to death, and—and something else. And *then* the very next day he disappears! But he hadn't planned to go on holiday, had he? I managed to prise that out of Hugo at least.'

'No.'

'And that's why I'm worried. Do you know what I really wish, Frosty? I wish he'd fall madly in love with another girl—any girl! I'd welcome her if she had . . . if she had square eyes and a crew cut!'

'No, you wouldn't. Besides, we wouldn't want him to be making any rash decisions right now.'

'What do you mean?'

'I think,' Miss Fortescue said mediatatively, 'that Rupert is right.'

'But . . .'

'No, what I mean is, I think Heather has finally made up her mind and Miles knows it. And it's time he accepted it and learnt to live with it. But it's got to be a danger period, hasn't it? A rebound period?'

Tallitha rested her brow against the door, then walked away quietly.

The rest of the afternoon was extremely busy, giving her not much time to think although it did occur to her that Heather Wentworth reminded her of one of those Russian dolls she'd read about once—you open one and there's another one inside, and then another.

When she got home she lay down on the settee feeling too exhausted even to change her clothes. But she couldn't stop herself from thinking.

Well I do see, she thought, echoing a phrase Miles had used, and his sister. I always did. And I decided we could still make a go of being married. Not only

because I love him and trust him—well, yes, because
of those things—but because I thought, better for it to
be me who understands and loves him.

She lay for a long time, staring at the ceiling with so
many images filtering through her mind. Christmas
Day for one. How right his sister was; he was very
good at covering up. Or perhaps I was so wrapped up
in my own misery that I didn't really look for it. But
then I've always known she must have been very, very
special . . .

Then a new thought rippled through her mind. Or
perhaps it wasn't so new; perhaps it had been there all
the time and only now found expression and brought
back memories of a girl who had been so shy and
gauche. Conscious of being acceptable only up to a
point—the housekeeper's daughter. They were different, the Gilmours, the Rathdowneys, the MacPhersons
and the Wentworths. They had an innate confidence
that came from years of social prominence and wealth.
And sometimes, Tallitha thought, I feel as if they're a
different breed from a girl with no background, no
roots, however much she thought she might have shed
the hayseeds—and never more so than this afternoon.
I feel like a stranger, an outsider looking in, fascinated
but knowing I'm not one of them, bewildered . . . The
same old story.

She turned her cheek on to the linen cushion and
closed her eyes. And a desperate yearning overcame
her for Miles to be beside her, so that she could take
her clothes off for him and love him as she'd never
done before, as he'd done for her once—to heal him
and take away the pain with her hands and her lips.

'Or take away my own?' she whispered into the
darkness.

*   *   *

She went in to work early the next morning.

There was a chance that Janet would be back. It had apparently only been a twenty-four-hour kind of virus that had claimed her so dramatically, and Tallitha found herself hoping devoutly that she would be back. Miles had been right, it had been a mistake to come to work, unless you looked at it from another angle.

She'd come in an hour early in the hope that she could hand over to Janet and leave; with no inkling of how brutally things were going to be sorted for her, once and for all. Before the blow fell, though, she found a letter in the express mail packet from Melbourne that was on her desk, addressed to her personally and privately, and she recognised Miles's handwriting. She opened it with trembling fingers but a little smile curved her lips as she read,

My dear Tallitha, I hope this reaches you and not Janet—not that there's any reason for her not to know, and as soon as possible, but I wouldn't like to shock her with my very private sentiments. How are you? I'm just about to go to bed—well, once I've got these off anyway. I have a hotel secretary standing by and incidentally, looking at me very disapprovingly. Can't imagine why I have this effect on secretaries! Would that you were here, but not for that purpose—I'm tired and irritable and lonely. In other words, needing you desperately. But the good news is that I expect to be home not tomorrow but the next day. Unfortunately, this business is a real débâcle and likely to send shock waves throughout the company—that's the bad news, from the point of view of how much work it's going to create for me when all I really want to do is spirit you away for an extended honeymoon. Where would you like to go, by the way? Think about it because, as soon as possible, that's what we will do. Must close now, reluctantly, or my martinet will walk out I suspect. I'm sure she has an inkling that this is not business. Just hope that she can't read my thoughts of what I'd like to be doing to you right now—but that you can. Love, Miles.

A tinge of pink entered Tallitha's cheeks but her eyes were soft as she folded the letter carefully and slipped it into her pocket.

Then she glanced up to see Leicester Rathdowney lounging in the doorway.

'Oh!' she said, then bit her lip. 'You're back,' she added lamely.

He straightened up and strolled over to her desk to sit on the edge of it. 'Yes,' he said, and his brown eyes slid over her in a way that made her shiver inwardly. 'I heard that you were back, too, Tallitha.' He picked up her paper knife and turned it over in his fingers.

Tallitha stared at the stainless steel knife in his hands and then looked up, and knew why she had shivered. For in those brown eyes, which had always repulsed her, there was now hatred and triumph, and she clenched her hands nervously in her lap because although she'd known that Les Rathdowney would find it hard to forgive her, she hadn't expected this. 'I've been hearing other things, too,' he drawled, still fiddling with the knife. 'How your great white boss has finally fallen on his face, for example.'

'What do you mean?' she whispered after a moment.

He shrugged. 'I thought it was common knowledge,' he said lazily. 'Miles has made a muck-up, hasn't he? I mean he's built this whole shopping centre project

STANDING ON THE OUTSIDE   159

around a construction company that's gone bust. That's a very basic mistake for him to have made and it's going to cost a lot of people a lot of money. Who would have thought it?' he said softly. 'Still stuck on him, by the way?'

Taillitha's lips parted but he didn't give her a chance to speak. 'Oh,' he stood up, 'and one other thing. During my . . . expulsion out west, I renewed an old acquaintanceship of mine. We were at school together. He was a little younger than I am but when I bumped into him in a Thargomindah pub he invited me back to the ranch for a few days. And, well, boys will be boys,' he said with a boyish grin that struck terror into Tallitha's heart. 'So we found ourselves swapping experiences.'

He paused and pursed his lips. 'Now it's not really so surprising, is it, Tallitha?' he said. 'Not surprising that I should have had a green-eyed, red-haired Tallitha Jones on my mind, don't you think?'

She closed her eyes.

'And not so surprising,' that mercilessly artless voice went on, 'that Brad Miller should find you hard to forget after what you tried to pin on him, is it?'

He waited in silence for a moment. Then, 'Is it, Tallitha? I wonder what Miles would think of you if he were to find out about it?'

Her eyelashes flew up and she parted her lips again, but Les intercepted her. 'For that matter, why stop at Miles? I'm sure there are a lot of people around here who would find it a lovely topic for discussion.'

She managed to speak at last, with difficulty. 'You wouldn't.'

Les Rathdowney laughed. 'Wouldn't I? I don't really know,' he said gaily. 'Or do I? Certainly if you were ever to provoke me again, Tallitha, I might find myself doing just that. Do we understand each other a little better now?'

His brown gaze flickered up and down her body meaningfully once again and she wanted to stand up and shout at him that he could do his worst. That he had no power at all to hurt her. And that if he was planning to use his hateful 'swapped experience'—she ground her teeth in shivering disgust at the thought of how he and Brad would have discussed her—to force her to accept his vengeful attentions, he was much mistaken.

But she said none of it. Instead she found herself thinking of two things—something Miles had said to her first. Not all men are gentlemen, Tallitha; one day you could get terribly hurt. How right you were, she marvelled. Because that's just what Leicester Rathdowney has in mind for me. I made myself a very bad enemy when I dented his vanity by making such a fool of him. As for Brad Miller, is he ever going to stop talking about me? I must have ... Well, events must have dented something of his very badly. His conscience, perhaps? But how right *I* was when I said something to Miles about stealing something much more valuable than the silver. Les can still hurt me, can't he? How much more is he going to hate me as Mrs Miles Gilmour? He'll hate Miles, and *use* my sordid—yes, sordid—past to Miles's disadvantage?

'Tallitha?'

She looked up blindly.

'I *said*, do we understand each other now?'

'Yes,' she said huskily, 'I think we do.'

'Good!' He put the paper knife down on the desk very gently. 'I'll be seeing you then.' And he walked out.

* * *

'Miss Fortescue, may I see you?' Tallitha asked about an hour later.

'Of course. Come in,' Miss Fortescue said, and Tallitha entered her office and looked around, thinking, this is where it all started. How curious . . .

'Sit down, Tallitha. I wanted to discuss whether you were going to hand over to Janet, as she's back, and continue your holiday, or whether you'd rather stay on through the worst of this crisis and take the holiday afterwards.'

'Miss Fortescue,' Tallitha said abruptly after a moment, 'is Mr Gilmour—I mean, what's happened? Is he going to be blamed for it?'

The older woman narrowed her eyes and frowned at Tallitha. Then she said, 'That's not something that concerns you or me, Tallitha.'

'I know, but I couldn't help wondering . . .'

Miss Fortescue considered for a long time. 'Personally,' she said at last, 'I have great faith in Mr Gilmour's capabilities. I rather thought you had, too.'

'I do,' Tallitha whispered, 'but I can't help wondering if this isn't going to cause him some . . . problems, some dissension on the board, perhaps.'

'It's a possibility,' Miss Fortescue admitted, then looked at Tallitha sternly. 'But what is it to you, Tallitha?'

'Nothing, I just wondered. Miss Fortescue, I actually wanted to see you about resigning. I have in fact already handed over to Janet. She came straight up to the office, so I went ahead. I could see that she's going to be able to cope. She's really a very bright, intelligent girl although I must admit I thought you'd made an odd choice to replace me at the time.' She tried to smile but it didn't come off very well, particularly as Miss Fortescue was now staring at her with a piercing acuteness. She knows, she thought. Somehow or other she's pieced it all together. But then I did give myself away when I told Susan Wentworth that Miles looked all right, didn't I? Because there was no way I could have known that, by Miss Fortescue's knowledge of the situation, anyway.

'Tallitha, is it that you're worried about your job as a result of this crisis?' Miss Fortescue asked.

'I . . . I . . . No.'

'Then there must be a reason for this very sudden decision to leave us in the lurch.'

Tallitha swallowed. 'I'm not doing that. You said yourself that Janet had been coping very well.'

'All the same, I'm sure Mr Gilmour will think you've left him in the lurch.'

'I have personal reasons for doing this, Miss Fortescue,' Tallitha stammered.

'Family reasons?'

'I . . . Yes.'

'I didn't think you had a family, Tallitha.'

Tallitha looked away and thought, oh, God, why didn't I just *go*?

'Or is it,' Miss Fortescue said quietly, 'that you've done the very thing I warned you not to as you sat in that very chair, and seemed so certain couldn't happen to you?'

Accounts, Personnel and the typing pool had never seemed so silent, Tallitha thought as she gazed through the half-glass walls. There were people moving about out there as usual but she couldn't hear them—it was like looking into a vast, silent aquarium inhabited by people, not fish.

'How did you know?' she asked painfully at last.

'I don't really know. It crossed my mind for the first time at the Christmas party, actually. I watched you dancing with him. I suppose, with the seed planted so to speak, it suddenly occurred to me that Mr . . . that Miles had taken a holiday to coincide with yours . . . not really coincidentally. Did you hear what his sister Susan had to say to me yesterday?'

'Yes. I listened at the door.'

'I wondered about that, too.' Miss Fortrescue grimaced.

'I'm sorry, so sorry,' Tallitha whispered.

'I would have done the same.'

Tallitha's eyes widened and Miss Fortescue smiled wryly. 'In fact, you probably don't know this but I went through the same thing with his father. I fell hopelessly in love with him, but he was very much in love with Miles's and Susan's mother and he was still in love with her memory to the day *he* died.' She looked down at the pink rosebud pinned to her lapel and then at Tallitha.

'I thought . . . I thought . . .' Tallitha stammered. 'I mean, there's a story floating around about that . . .'

'Is there? Well of course there probably would be. It's my one sentimental weakness, I guess.' She smiled slightly. 'I worked for him for a long time and when he found out when my birthday was, he used to send me pink rosebuds every year.'

'Did he know?'

'I think he did towards the end. We were very close in a purely platonic way.'

Tallitha blinked several times then dropped her head into her hands and started to cry.

'You mustn't be sad for me, my dear,' Miss Fortescue said finally.

'I can't help it,' Tallitha wept.

'Nor should you confuse your situation with mine. There might be some parallels, but . . .'

'Some?' Tallitha said a little bitterly and blew her nose. 'You know how he feels about Heather Wentworth. Because he can't have her doesn't necessarily mean he's going to stop wanting her. You told me yourself he was very like his father.'

'Tallitha . . .'

'But that's not all. I think Susan summed it up rather well yesterday—I feel, in their company, a bit like a square-eyed, crew-cut freak.'

'That's nonsense,' Miss Fortescue objected sharply.

'Is it?' Tallitha said with a sad little smile.

'Tallitha, tell me what *has* happened between you and Miles.'

'He has'—she closed her eyes briefly—'among other things, asked me to marry him. You see, he came straight to me on Christmas Day, but I didn't know, didn't guess what had happened . . . until it was too late.'

Miss Fortescue was silent for a time, then she said, 'If he's asked you to marry him you *mustn't* take into account anything you overheard. That's only Susan's and my reading of things. You must make your own, Tallitha.'

'I have. Don't think I haven't,' she said shakily. 'But it reads the same, only worse. I have some information on the subject you and his sister don't, yet.'

Miss Fortescue stared at her and started to speak but obviously changed tack as Tallitha tensed convulsively. 'So you're running away from him. Do you think that's fair?'

'Yes, actually I think it's the fairest thing I can do. *You* must know how impossible it is to talk Miles out of anything once he's made up his mind.'

'But if he's asked you to marry him, he must have

his reasons. I know, I know I was talking—and you can't imagine how sincerely I regret it—about him being on the rebound, but I also can't imagine him fooling around with your life on a whim. Can you?'

'No. I think he probably plans to make me his life's . . . work, and I'm sure he'd stand by me whatever the cost. Would you care to be in that position? Or see someone you loved in it?'

CHAPTER EIGHT

'THAT'LL be costing you sixty-five cents, love, but they're best quality oranges, that I can guarantee!'

Tallitha agreed that they were beautiful oranges and walked out of the little fruit shop she patronised, calling good night to the elderly Greek owner who liked nothing better than to chat with his clients. He's probably as lonely as I am, she'd thought once or twice.

She walked home slowly in the gathering dusk, down a steep street in Elizabeth Bay on Sydney Harbour, reluctant to go home to her newly acquired, impersonal, furnished flat in an elderly but well-cared-for building where most of the tenants were elderly, too, and often suspicious of young faces.

In fact, in the last months since her flight from Brisbane, she had come to the conclusion that there were a lot of lonely people in Sydney. But perhaps that was true of all big cities. Yet it frightened Tallitha often. So many people teeming into and out of town, suburbs stretching for miles, underground trains, traffic . . . and not a soul that she really knew.

Perhaps I'm more of a country girl at heart than I suspected, she pondered. Or perhaps Brisbane is just a nice size for a city because it didn't seem to frighten me as Sydney does. Or perhaps . . .

But she always tried to cut off her thoughts at that point, thoughts of that last frantic day in Brisbane, of Miss Fortescue pleading with her not to do anything rash—as if to let Miles Gilmour marry her would not be the rashest act she could ever commit! Of how Miss

Fortescue had then insisted on personally typing out a reference for her—an agonisingly slow process, or so it had seemed to Tallitha, who was desperately afraid Miles would ring. Possibly that's exactly what Miss Fortescue had been hoping for.

But she had finally escaped. She hadn't really wanted to accept the reference, but on that point Miss Fortescue had been adamant. 'And *use* it,' she had said, 'if you need to. Jobs aren't that easy to come by, particularly if you can't demonstrate that you've had previous experience.'

As soon as she'd got home, Tallitha had rung the second-hand furniture man from the phone box and begged him to come and take her furniture away that very morning for the price he'd quoted her—a lower price than she'd thought she could wangle from him with time. And when he had been and gone, she had sat on the floor of her empty flat and started to laugh at the incongruities of life. Why on earth, when she'd been planning to marry Miles Gilmour, had she bothered with beating a few more dollars out of a second-hand furniture dealer? To laugh, and then to cry . . .

But by six o'clock that evening she had been on board the southbound train for Sydney—or God knew where, it hadn't seemed to matter all that much—with only her books and her clothes, and Mason, stowed in the deepest gloom in the luggage van amid baskets of cats and cages of dogs. Oh, Mason, the things I do to you. Is it any wonder you don't talk?

She had spent the next night at the People's Palace in Sydney, too depressed to *be* depressed by it. But the next morning she had taken hold and taken stock and, by that evening, had found herself a room in a boarding-house.

During the next few months she'd taken a succession of waitressing and menial jobs because she'd been determined not to live off her savings, and determined not to use her reference for as long as possible.

They had been bitter months in many ways. Months of wondering, amidst every other lonely emotion she experienced, if she hadn't been the most abject fool. In fact, she could think of only two things that had brightened those months, although the second of them had been a bittersweet one. But the very simple explanation for Mason's lack of speech had quite delighted her. When a bleak winter was finally loosening its grip, came a chance reading of a small item in a newspaper. The managing director of a well-known and reputedly solid, Melbourne-based construction company, it said, had been committed for trial on charges of fraud and embezzlement which had directly contributed to the company's collapse.

Tallitha recognised the name of the company only too well, with a sigh of relief. Thank God, she thought, they can't blame Miles for that. But I *knew* there had to be an explanation of some kind! And whether it was spring, or whether it was reading that article, she came to a decision—to get herself a better job and a better lifestyle.

The job she got was with a firm of accountants and she used her reference from Rathdowney, MacPherson & Gilmour to get it. She was also quite honest with herself —perhaps, as Miss Fortescue had intended it to be, the reference was the one slender link she had left with Miles. If he chose, if he hadn't seen the wisdom of what she'd done, he could trace her through it. And she was honest enough to admit that, in her heart of hearts, she desperately wanted him to.

It was like the last seed of hope that she just couldn't eradicate with all the logic in the world—a tiny prayer for a miracle.

One month later that precious seed had withered and died. She hadn't cried; she had moved into the relative comfort of her new flat and been amazed that she should have given it a month, or allowed herself to foster doubts that the firm she was now working for wouldn't have checked it out. Because it would be highly unlikely, she knew, for a firm of meticulous accountants not to check out the integrity of prospective staff, even secretaries.

Now it was summer and Elizabeth Bay was quiet and fragrant on a dusky Friday evening, and you would never imagine that the garish nightlife of King's Cross was just over the hill. Tallitha stopped and breathed deeply and closed her eyes. If I can just get through tomorrow, she thought, that will be a true test . . .

She turned and went into her block of flats.

She worked a half-day on Saturdays, until one, and this was a particularly busy Saturday for which she was grateful. But at one o'clock she stepped out into Macquarie Street, breathed deeply and started to walk blindly, because she knew there was no way she could go home.

She walked past the pink, restored Mint and round the Hyde Park Barracks and found herself in the Domain without recalling crossing any streets. And she kept on walking, past the Art Gallery and into the Botanic Gardens because walking seemed to be the only way she could hold at bay a sea of misery.

There weren't many people around as she wandered down mysterious paths between tall banks of mysterious foliage—Sunday was the day the people of Sydney enjoyed their beautiful Botanic Gardens to the full, and picnicked, beneath spreading old trees and amidst great beds of flowers where ibis roamed tamely, on the lawns that swept down to Farm Cove.

She walked down to the stone wall of the cove and shivered suddenly, for the sun had gone in behind a capricious spring thundercloud that cast an eerie blue light over Sydney Harbour and the bridge, and on nearby Bennelong Point and the sails of the Opera House.

She took another deep breath but the tears came all the same and she dashed at them furiously and turned to start walking again, anywhere. But there was a man standing behind her, just a foot or so away, a tall man with dark hair and dark blue eyes, and she stared at him through a mist of tears.

Then she said brokenly, 'Oh, Miles, you came . . .'

'Yes,' he agreed very quietly. 'Happy birthday, Tallitha.'

'I . . . I was trying to forget it,' she wept into her hands.

'Because of me?'

'Because I'm a fool.'

'Oh no,' he said grimly, and took her into his arms. 'Not you. Don't,' he murmured into her hair, and held her shaking body very close.

'Yes, I am. I should never have let you find me. S-sorry, but it seems I can't stop loving you.'

'You don't have to—I wish I could make you understand.'

'I do, that's the trouble. How did you . . .'

'I was waiting outside your office. I followed you. Look—Hell!'

She lifted her head as he tightened his arms around

her and a great clap of thunder followed the streak of lightning he must have seen. She buried her face in his shoulder and clung to him as another clap split the air and the heavens opened to dump pelting, hissing rain on the path all around them, obliterating the harbour and the lawns and the Opera House.

Then he was saying, 'Come,' urgently, and she was stumbling along beside him, holding on to his arm with both hands.

They ran up the path past the Opera House and down towards Circular Quay. 'It's not far to my hotel,' he said into her ear, stopping briefly to put his arm around her. 'Think you can make it? Because I don't think any taxi is going to pick us up—we're too wet. Or would you like to shelter somewhere?'

'I . . . Not really,' she panted as a fork of jagged lightning lit up the street. 'I'd like to get right out of it.'

The hotel wasn't far and the foyer was like a haven of softly-lit safety as the commissionaire, who obviously knew Miles, ran out to meet them with an umbrella. 'Mr Gilmour, sir! Wherever have you been?'

'Out walking,' Miles said wryly. 'Can you get my key for me? I'd like to soak as little of your foyer as possible.'

Tallitha didn't really have time to catch her breath until the door of his suite closed behind them. Then, as Miles went over to close the curtains, she looked down at herself and gasped, because her pretty yellow spring outfit had shrunk and moulded itself to her body like a second skin.

'Oh God, what do I look like?' She raised horrified green eyes.

'Stunning,' Miles said, coming back towards her

with a grin. 'Why do you think I got you up here with all speed? I thought you might create a riot.'

Tallitha blushed vividly and he laughed softly and took her hand to lead her into the bedroom. 'There's only one thing to do—shed them and have a shower.'

'But I haven't got anything . . .'

'There's a robe behind the door. Do it,' he gave her a gentle shove. 'You look frozen.'

The towelling robe she put on after a fumbling shower—she didn't seem to be able to co-ordinate her movements too well, let alone her thoughts—had the hotel emblem on the breast pocket and was miles too big for her, with the sleeves coming down over her hands. But she tucked them up, then stared at herself in the mirror for a few moments. Her hair was still damp and curling riotously, and her eyes were very green and shadowed in the pale oval of her face.

But finally she persuaded herself to leave the bathroom, to find that Miles had changed into his own robe, that he had conjured up afternoon tea with scones and pikelets set out on a trolley. He had closed the bedroom curtains too and switched on the lamps so that the luxurious room glowed softly, and the sounds of the storm were muted.

'That's better,' he said turning towards her. 'Feeling warmer?'

'Yes.'

'Come here,' he said softly.

'Miles . . .' Her voice shook.

'I haven't really had a chance to wish you happy birthday,' he said with a slight smile and moved towards her. 'Your birthdays always seem to be traumatic occasions, don't they? How are you?' he added huskily, and took her clenching hands into his.

'I'm fine,' she whispered after a moment, but her green eyes were painfully confused and tense.

'Are you wondering why I took so long to come?'

She licked her lips and trembled.

'I was in America on a business trip. I'd put off going for as long as I could, and my trusted ally, Miss Fortescue, chose the time to fall down and break her hip. She was off for nearly a month in traction.' As he spoke he released her hands and drew her into his arms. 'Thank God, your reference was referred to Janet and she made a note of it for me when I got back. Promise me just one thing, Tallitha. Don't ever run away from me again. Whatever happens, don't do that.' And he held her with a kind of fearful intensity that almost took her breath away.

Later she said tearfully, 'I thought it was the best thing to do. I still . . .'

'Don't understand, do you?' he said. 'And I can't blame you.' His lips twisted. 'Will you let me try to explain about Heather?'

She tried not to, but tensed slightly.

'Look, why don't you hop into bed—no, I'm not going to leap on you,' he said with a lurking smile, but his hand on her cheek. 'But it's a good place to be on a day like this. I'll pour you a cup of tea.'

The bed was where she ended up, comfortably curled up against the pillows, sipping her tea but with her eyes still watchful and wary.

'I suppose,' he said finally, standing beside the trolley with a cup in his hands and his head bent over it, 'Heather is the best place to start, although we have other matters to sort out.' He looked up suddenly. 'And you were right when you assumed I'd asked you to marry me in spite of the fact that I was still in love with her, or thought I was.' His mouth set in a grim line for a moment. 'You were all right. Yes, Frosty told me everything—what Susan had said and so on. But what no one was to know was that the moment I sat down and acknowledged that I might not be able to *find* you, it occurred to me that I'd been in love with the wrong woman. That while Heather had undoubtedly been the source of my greatest frustration, you were the source of my greatest joy; that you had given me more pleasure, more sweet, undemanding love than I'd ever deserved. And that it wasn't only concern for you, and guilt, that was driving me mad, but a sense of loss and love almost too much to bear.'

'Miles, you don't . . .'

'Yes I do,' he said positively. 'I have to try to explain why I didn't understand until it was too late. Why I did the unforgivable—took another woman to try and make myself forget Heather. I think it all hinges on the fact that I've been singularly spoiled. Everything I'd ever wanted in my life, I'd got. Oh, I didn't get it all on a platter, but the other things I worked for and got. For example, my father told me it wouldn't be fair to expect to walk into his shoes without proving my worth, so I set about doing that. I went to England and got a degree there good enough to land me an excellent job which gave me the opportunity to study the European Economic Community. I also got on to the board of that company entirely through my own efforts. When I came home eventually, I was asked to sit in on a joint parliamentary committee set up to study the effects of the Common Market on Australian agriculture, and got a directorship of a finance company.

'All of it was the perfect background to taking over from my father and for wresting Rathdowney, MacPherson & Gilmour into the latter half of the twentieth century, and building it into a company that could take its place beside the likes of Elders and so on. All of it came, except . . .'

'Except Heather?' Tallitha murmured.

'Except Heather. I let her slip through my fingers once, and lost her. When I first went overseas I wanted her to come with me, I wanted us to get married. I was twenty-three odd, she was nineteen. But her parents were dead against it and they prevailed. Too young, they said to both of us. Spread your wings first. And her father took me aside for a man-to-man chat and pointed out that I'd probably dominated Heather's girlish thoughts since her early teens, which struck an unfortunate chord from my point of view, because from *my* late teens I'd had an inkling that I was going to fall in love with Heather. By the time she was sixteen it was no longer only an inkling, but I held off. I was also well into the process of spreading *my* wings, as young men do,' he said with a bitter little smile. 'But something always drew me back to Heather—there was something about her I couldn't find in anyone else. And I looked rather hard for it. Perhaps I had a presentiment,' he said ironically. 'Anyway, I watched and waited, and then, when she was about eighteen-and-a-half, I started to court her very gently. She was—I don't know how, they weren't precisely Victorian times—but she was like my own creation, I suppose. Virginal and very shy, but opening up like a flower, just for me.'

'What happened?' Tallitha asked huskily.

'The usual,' he said after a while. 'During that man-to-man chat, I lost my temper. I told her father any idiot could see we were made for each other, and I told him how long I'd already been waiting for Heather. He was shocked to the core—he was always a pious, suspicious old coot with a talent for making money that was positively indecent. I mean it just didn't fit in with his holier-than-thou sentiments. But be that as it may, he then accused me of having already ravished her, as he put it, which infuriated me all the more because I hadn't. So we had a right royal row in which every grudge every MacPherson had held against every Gilmour surfaced. And there'd been plenty.'

'Oh, no,' Tallitha whispered.

'Oh, yes. Unfortunately, Heather and her mother were listening outside the door by this time, and Heather's mother rang my father and demanded that he come over and do something—she believed her husband had a weak heart, which I never saw the slightest sign of—and my father came, and then Hugo and his wife arrived and, well, talk of the Montagues and the Capulets!—you want to see the MacPhersons and the Rathdowneys and Gilmours have a free-for-all.'

Tallitha bit her lip. What happened then?'

He sat down on the side of the bed. 'What happened then?' he said drily. 'Looking back now I can tell you what really happened then. At the time I wasn't thinking too straight. If I'd had a white horse I'd have swept Heather up and taken her away, whatever she wanted. But the general consensus was that we should wait. Even my father thought so, and he warned me to think hard before I caused a rift between Heather and her father, because the old bastard was very well known for *never* changing his mind or going back on his word. Did I want to alienate her from her father for ever? That kind of thing.' He smiled slightly. 'At that point in time it was *exactly* what I wanted,' he said wryly. 'But Heather, God bless her,' he said with a sudden softening of his eyes, 'was totally confused.

Even I could see that, although it didn't help. What I wasn't to know was how easy it was to confuse Heather.'

'So you went overseas alone?'

'Yes. I bowed to pressure and did just that, rather brutally, I'm afraid.'

'Oh, Miles,' Tallitha said softly with tears running down her cheeks, 'you hurt her.'

'Yes. Look, I'm not telling you this to make you cry,' he said in sudden exasperation and pulled her on to his lap. 'In fact I'm beginning to wonder if I'm doing my cause any good by telling you at all.'

She had to laugh a little ruefully. 'Sorry, but it's so sad and . . . moving.'

'Sounds as if it could have come right out of the movies, too, I guess.'

'No it doesn't. Knowing you and them, I can just imagine it. I didn't know Heather's father, of course, but all of you that I do know . . .'

'Don't go on, I get your drift,' he said with an ironic twist of his lips, then he kissed her tears. 'Well, if you're sure you can stand to hear the rest?' She nodded against his chest. 'I went overseas in a peculiar frame of mind, as you can imagine. I'd left behind the impression that I was a raving Don Juan; I'd left Heather hurt and bewildered; I was, to put it mildly, as confused as any bloody one of them. But I did have one conviction—that Heather was mine and that it was just a matter of time, it just *couldn't* be any other way. I was counting on a year for them to come round, but ten months after I left my father wrote and told me that Heather, apparently of her own free will, had married Rupert's bloody brother. Which made sense of some of the veiled remarks it would have taken Sherlock Holmes to unravel, that Susan had made in her letters. Susan,' he marvelled, 'my usually beautifully if not brutally frank sister, had seen it coming and not really known how to tell me.'

'Perhaps she knew how angry you'd be?'

'Perhaps,' he agreed with a lift of his eyebrows. 'And I was, but not with Heather. I could have killed Hayden Wentworth, though, and as for MacPherson—after sanctimoniously warning *me* off because she was too young and then giving her on a platter to someone like Hayden—all I could imagine was that he'd done it as a personal gibe at me. Here, take that, you young whippersnapper of a *Gilmour* ... Oh God!' he said, laughing despite himself and rocking Tallitha in his arms. 'What a fool I was!'

'But it was none of those things?' Tallitha asked eventually.

'No, not really. Just as I had, Hayden fell in love with her, I think, and swept her off her feet.'

'I think so, too—that he really loves her. I saw him looking at her at the dance. He was so concerned about her.'

'Yes,' Miles agreed thoughtfully.

Tallitha stirred in his arms. 'But she wasn't happy with him?'

He sighed. 'No. And do you know why? I think they were right, she was too young. She wasn't ready for either of us. I think the very depth of Hayden's feelings for her frightened her a bit, and whenever I came home, it was almost impossible to avoid them and ... well, I couldn't hide the fact that I felt cheated sometimes, which made her feel guilty and even more unsure of herself. None of which was lost on Hayden, of course. I suppose, because of how he felt about her, he went on the defensive with her. Between us, we must have made her life hell, which was crazy, but that's how it was. And to her credit, although she did tell me once she thought she might have married the wrong man, she always held her marriage vows sacred. She was a true MacPherson about that.'

Tallitha stirred again. 'You mean . . .?'

'Yes. I never slept with Heather. Although, when she said that . . . But that wasn't how I wanted her, as someone else's wife. Not for myself or for her.'

'I knew that,' Tallitha whispered.

He grimaced. 'I don't see how you could have. There were so many crazy rumours floating around.'

'It just didn't sound like you, to me. I . . . Of all the reasons I had for leaving, that wasn't one of them.'

'I'm glad,' he said simply. 'But let me finish. That day, when she came to see me in the office, it was to tell me that she hoped she was pregnant because she'd finally woken up to the fact that her life had to go one way or the other; and that Hayden loved her and that of her own free will, she'd given him the right to. I accused her of loving both of us; it amounted to that, although I didn't put it quite so pleasantly. She said she thought it was probably true, she was just one of those foolish women, but that with a baby on the way she had to put her life in order. And for the first time she spoke with real conviction.

'What I didn't realise, until Christmas Day, was that not only had she woken up to the fact that she couldn't go on drifting between the two of us, but that she was finally *really* waking up to love—his. Perhaps she hadn't seen it coming herself, but I could see it. And now I can only be genuinely happy for her.'

There was silence apart from the rain drumming on the windows. Not torrential rain any more, but a steady downpour.

Then he said in a different voice, 'That was strange

really because the same awakening finally happened for me. Perhaps, although I wouldn't ever want to go through it again, you did the right thing when you ran away. It made the scales fall from my eyes.'

'That wasn't why I did it.'

'I know, you did it because you thought I couldn't ever change, but you were wrong. You see, all of a sudden I understood that whatever it was I'd felt for Heather had grown out of all proportion on account of my ego, circumstance and unattainability. *Those* things became an end in themselves. And the rest of it was an attraction to a quality she had . . . of a beautiful page to be written on, for want of better words to describe it. Can you understand that?'

'Miles . . .' She trembled in his arms.

'Listen, just listen. I *love* you. I've felt sick every day since you left. Not sick with pride and revenge; sick with fear that I'd never find you, and if I did, never be able to make you understand. I only missed you by a couple of hours, probably. When I rang in about lunchtime that day, my call was immediately switched to Miss Fortescue and she told me what had happened. I came home on the next plane and spent all night scouring the bus stations and trains.'

Tallitha lifted her face and he kissed her lips gently.

'I've also,' he said unsteadily, 'been a great trial to everyone who knows me ever since, and as for those who work for me, they hate me. Given time I'd have had no one left.'

'Oh, Miles,' she whispered with a smile trembling on her lips.

'It's true,' he vowed. 'Even Janet gets around me with an invisible chair in her hand like a lady lion-tamer.'

Tallitha giggled and he kissed her again.

Then she sobered and reached out and pleated the cuff of his robe. 'I . . . I left for another reason, too,' she said. 'One you might not know about.' She took a deep breath. 'Les Rathdowney found out about Brad. They went to school together, and they met up when you sent him out west. It . . . it seems I'm still something of a talking point.' Her voice shook. 'Les mentioned it to me when I went back to work after you'd gone to Melbourne.'

Miles went very still. Then he said, 'So?' And his voice was harsh.

Tallitha shivered, 'Miles, I couldn't help knowing that Les hated you, and that he was jealous and that he wouldn't have hesitated to use it if we'd got married. Soon everyone would have known about my sordid past. I could just imagine his mother's reaction, everyone's—your sister, too. He's diabolically clever that way,' she said a little feverishly. 'I didn't think I could stand it, and I was afraid it would hurt you.' She hid her face against his arm.

'Tallitha,' Miles said, and took her by the shoulders, 'look at me.'

Her lashes swept up finally and all the old, shrinking, naked hurt was in her eyes, as Les Rathdowney had been able to rekindle it. 'Oh, God,' Miles said huskily, 'have I ever shown you that it means a damn thing to me? Ever?'

Her lips quivered. 'No. But if you were always having to defend me, it might. And if . . . if there are divisions between you and the Rathdowneys . . .'

'The only divisions,' he interrupted, 'exist in Les's imagination—I know his mother is ambitious for him and I know there *were* divisions, but between the MacPhersons and the Gilmours, not the Gilmours and the Rathdowneys. In fact, Hugo and I have a perfect working relationship and he's quite alive to his son's imperfections. Hugo's actually a realist behind some of his odder affectations. Why do you think he virtually gave me *carte blanche* with the company? And supported me totally over the shopping centre fiasco? He knew as well as I, by the way . . .'

'I know,' she whispered. 'I read it in the paper.'

'Well, he knew that something extremely fishy had to have happened.'

Tallitha's lips parted. 'I didn't realise.'

'As for your past, the most important person it could affect, perhaps, already knows about it and she's a hundred per cent on your side.'

Tallitha's eyes widened.

'I'm talking about Susan,' Miles said. 'I was absolutely furious with her when Frosty told me what had happened, and I confronted her and accused her of . . . well, a lot of things, but of being a meddlesome busybody primarily. I guess I was pretty forceful because she finally accused me of having fallen head over heels in love with my Miss Jones, as she put it.'

Tallitha tensed inwardly.

'I agreed with her,' he said, holding her closer, 'and then she wanted to know everything, so I told her everything. Including the reason why, although I didn't know about Les, you might have thought you weren't good enough for the Gilmours. Frosty mentioned that you'd said something about feeling inferior——' He kissed her quite fiercely this time.

'Susan,' he said eventually as she lay a little breathless in his arms, 'gave me a message for you, if ever I found you. She said to tell you something similar had happened to her. I never knew.' He looked down at her with a frown of pain in his eyes. 'She hid it even from me, which makes me feel bad, even though I was only nineteen at the time.

'When she was twenty-one, she fell in love with a married man, and fell pregnant. He was horrified and persuaded her to have an abortion and after she had, he dumped her. She said she felt as if her whole life had fallen apart, as if she would never forgive herself for not keeping her baby, and as if she'd really let herself down. It was only Rupert, she said, who seemed to love her despite it all, including a period of intense cynicism she went through—I can imagine her giving him hell,' he said with a slight smile. 'But it was Rupert who taught her to believe in herself again. And she has, I know for a fact, been happily married to him ever since.'

Tallitha closed her eyes.

'The thing is,' he said intently, 'do you honestly think Susan would have asked me to tell you something like that, her darkest secret, if she hadn't been prepared to accept you and wasn't convinced I was totally in love with you?'

'I . . .' Tallitha whispered.

'And if you don't believe I can handle Les, believe me, Susan can. *And* his mother.'

'I believe you,' Tallitha said shyly and breathlessly.

'Does that mean you're going to marry me? Perhaps I should point out at this stage,' he said with his eyes glinting wickedly in a way she remembered so well, and loved, 'that you have no choice now.'

'Oh?'

'No. Your clothes are ruined by the look of them, so you'll just have to stay here with me for as long as I like—a prisoner of love, until you say yes. And I know just how to achieve that. I'll make love to you until you beg for mercy and agree to anything I propose, Miss Jones.'

'In that case,' she answered demurely but with her green eyes alight with love and laughter, 'prepare yourself for a long siege, because I rather like the sound of that.'

'How am I going?' he asked a long time afterwards.

Tallitha was lying in his arms, filled with the delicious feeling of lassitude of someone who had been thoroughly made love to.

'Splendidly,' she murmured and smoothed her palm down his arm. 'Even better than I remember,' she said wonderingly.

'That's what celibacy does for you,' he said wryly. 'Perhaps we should declare periods of our marriage celibate?'

'I'd rather not,' she whispered with a grin, and he hugged her.

'What shall we do?' he asked after a while.

'I thought we'd decided that?'

'I mean, should we order dinner before we make love again, or afterwards? Because I intend to order a celebration dinner, you see. It's still your birthday, among other things.'

'So much for your periods of celibacy,' she teased, and then sat up suddenly. 'Oh!'

'What?' He raised himself on one elbow and looked comically worried.

'Well, it's Mason, actually. I'd forgotten. I might be able to survive this siege, but I don't know if Mason can.'

'Mason!' he said. 'Hell, I'd forgotten about Mason. Is he talking yet? Because if he's not by now I doubt if he ever will.'

'Mason,' she said mysteriously, 'is another case of a deep, dark secret.'

'He is?'

'She. He's a she.'

'*He's* a she?'

'She's a she.' Tallitha giggled. 'She always was. That's why she can't talk! It's only the males who do.'

'Then . . .'

'I got sold a pup when I bought her . . .'

'My dear Tallitha,' he interrupted her incredulously, 'I'm totally confused now.'

'Oh, you *know* what I mean! I thought I was buying a boy budgie but it was a girl. You can tell, if you know what to look for, by that bit on the top of their beaks. It should be blue!'

'And hers isn't?'

'No. Do you know, I swear she's been happier since I found out and stopped expecting miracles from her. Which is why . . .'

'I see. But will she starve in one night?'

'No,' Tallitha said consideringly.

'Then come back here,' he commanded softly.

She lay back in his arms. 'What we'll do is, tomorrow I'll personally go and collect Mason and anything else you need, so that you can go out and about decently. How's that?'

'So much for your sieges,' she said against the corner of his mouth. 'Oh, God, I love you.'

They did have a candlelit dinner.

'Did Heather have a boy or a girl?' Tallitha asked as she sipped champagne.

'Both,' Miles said.

'You mean . . .?' Tallitha stared at him with her glass held aloft and her eyes round.

'Mmm, twins. They seem to run in the Wentworth clan. She's very happy.'

'Oh, I'm so glad,' Tallitha said softly.

He smiled at her across the table and reached out to cover her free hand with his. 'When are you going to marry me?'

'As soon as possible.'

'That's good, because as a matter of fact, twins aren't unknown in the Gilmour family. I'm surprised Susan only had one set.'

'Oh! Now you tell me!'

'Come here.'

She went and curled up in his lap. 'Something else I forgot to tell you. Diana has met a young man who wants to marry her.'

'Di . . . How do you know?'

'I tracked her down, thinking you might keep in touch with her.'

Tallitha blinked away a tear. 'I was afraid to. Oh, I'm so happy for her!' she said fervently.

'There's going to be one problem, though, persuading her father to let her and Amanda go.'

'*Honestly!*' Tallitha said exasperatedly.

'Mmm. Life wasn't meant to be simple. She sent you a message, too.'

The way he said it caused Tallitha to tilt her head back to look up at him. 'What?'

'I don't think I should repeat it,' he said gravely.

'Why not?' she asked suspiciously.

'Well,' he shrugged, 'all right, if you insist. She said to tell you you were mad to turn your back on a man of my looks, nature and . . .'

'I get it—don't go on,' she warned. 'You'll get a swollen head. And as for that perfectly smug look in your eye . . .!'

'What are you going to do about it?' he drawled.

'I'll think of something—just wait until I get some

clothes!' she threatened, and he immediately looked so abjectly rueful that they started to laugh.

'You know,' he said finally, 'I've told you a lot of things tonight—about Heather mainly—but I haven't told you why I love you. Only that I do.'

'Why?' she whispered.

He was silent for a time, then he said abruptly, 'Because I admire you more than any woman I've ever known. I told you that at the Christmas party I sensed . . . something. I think that was my first intimation not only that I could be attracted to you, but that there was something about you I really admired and respected. Something fired and fine and tempered but very human; something warm but locked in—I suspect I'm going to be attracted to that mysterious combination for the rest of my life,' he finished very quietly and slid his hand beneath her robe so that his palm lay on her nipple and his long fingers curved under her arm, cupping her breast.

She trembled. 'I thought once before that I could have died quite happily just because I was close to you,' she said huskily. 'But that was nothing to how I feel now. What can I say in return?'

'You don't have to,' he murmured with a smile curving his lips. 'You could show me instead.'

She did.

ROMANCE

Variety is the spice of romance

Each month, Mills & Boon publish new romances. New stories about people falling in love. A world of variety in romance — from the best writers in the romantic world. Choose from these titles in November.

STANDING ON THE OUTSIDE Lindsay Armstrong
DARK ENCHANTMENT Helen Bianchin
THE DECEPTION TRAP Ann Charlton
DON'T ASK ME NOW Emma Darcy
IMMUNE TO LOVE Claudia Jameson
A REASON FOR MARRIAGE Penny Jordan
CONTRASTS Rowan Kirby
A LONG WAY FROM HEAVEN Susanne McCarthy
BRITTANY'S CASTLE Leigh Michaels
JUNGLE ISLAND Kay Thorpe
*DIAMOND VALLEY Margaret Way
*PASSION'S DAUGHTER Sara Wood

On sale where you buy paperbacks. If you require further information or have any difficulty obtaining them, write to: Mills & Boon Reader Service, PO Box 236, Thornton Road, Croydon, Surrey CR9 3RU, England.

*These two titles are available *only* trom Mills & Boon Reader Service.

Mills & Boon the rose of romance

From the author of Gypsy comes a spellbinding romance.

WORLDWIDE

A SPELLBINDING ROMANCE FROM THE AUTHOR
OF THE BESTSELLING 'GYPSY'

Carole Mortimer

She offered him the magic with which
to mend his shattered dreams

Unresistingly drawn into Rand's arms, Merlyn then had to suffer his rejection, as he retreated into his own private torment where he still grieved the loss of his beautiful and talented wife, Suzie.

How would Merlyn then persuade him that she would be right to play Suzie in a film based on the actress's life?

It took an unseen hand to make Rand aware of Merlyn's own special kind of magic.

**ANOTHER BESTSELLER
FROM
CAROLE MORTIMER**

W()RLDWIDE

ACCEPT 4
MILLS & BOON
ROMANCES
ABSOLUTELY FREE

...after all, what better way to continue your enjoyment of the finest stories from the world's foremost romantic authors? This is a very special introductory offer designed for regular readers. Once you've read your four **free** books you can take out a subscription (although there's no obligation at all). Subscribers enjoy many special benefits and all these are described overleaf. ▶▶▶